Translations of Mathematical Monographs Volume 9

Soluble and Nilpotent
LINEAR GROUPS

by

D. Suprunenko

AMERICAN MATHEMATICAL SOCIETY
PROVIDENCE, RHODE ISLAND
1963

РАЗРЕШИМЫЕ И НИЛЬПОТЕНТНЫЕ
ЛИНЕЙНЫЕ ГРУППЫ

Д. А. СУПРУНЕНКО

Издательство
Белгосуниверситета имени В. И. Ленина
Минск 1958

Translated by K. A. Hirsch

Publication aided by a grant from the
NATIONAL SCIENCE FOUNDATION

Library of Congress Card Number 63-20676

Printed in the United States of America

To the Revered Memory
of my Father
Alekseĭ Emel′janovič Suprunenko

Contents

Introduction

The group of all nonsingular linear transformations of an n-dimensional linear space over a field P is called the *full linear group over* P.

One of the oldest problems in the theory of groups going back to Galois, is the problem of the construction of all soluble groups of substitutions, which has led to the investigation of subgroups of the full linear group over a finite field. The first book devoted to linear groups was the celebrated *Traité des substitutions* by Jordan. Jordan's book contains a vast number of results on the theory of substitution groups, on the theory of quadratic forms, on the theory of matrices (here one finds the well-known normal Jordan form); but its main part is concerned with the structure of soluble subgroups of the full linear group over a finite field.

Subsequently, soluble subgroups of a full linear group over a finite field were investigated by O. Ju. Schmidt, Bucht and many other authors.

Like Jordan, Schmidt and Bucht carried out their investigations in direct connection with the Galois problem mentioned above.

Soluble subgroups of a full linear group over an algebraically closed field were discussed by Zassenhaus in connection with investigations on discrete linear groups. Zassenhaus proved that every subgroup of the full linear group has a maximal soluble normal subgroup. He also proved that locally soluble linear groups are soluble and that the length of the derived series of a soluble linear group of fixed degree is bounded.

In recent decades, algebraists have been much occupied with abstract soluble and nilpotent groups. Here, the most significant results are due to A. I. Mal′cev, S. N. Černikov, O. Ju. Schmidt, R. Baer, K. A. Hirsch, V. M. Gluškov, and B. I. Plotkin.

In connection with the structure of certain classes of soluble abstract groups Mal′cev discussed a number of properties of soluble linear groups and proved the theorem that a soluble group of matrices over an algebraically closed field has a normal subgroup of finite index whose matrices can be reduced simultaneously to triangular form.

The author of the present book has made an attempt in his articles [**15**; **16**; **23**] to develop a systematic investigation of linear soluble groups under various assumptions about the ground field P. The following cases are discussed: (1) P is an arbitrary field, (2) P is a finite field, (3) P is an algebraically closed field, (4) P is the field of real numbers. In a number of other papers we have studied nilpotent subgroups of the full linear group (see [**17-22**; **24**]).

The present work essentially represents a synthesis of all the author's papers on linear soluble and on linear nilpotent groups.

Being concerned with soluble subgroups of the full linear group we pay attention principally to maximal soluble subgroups. Since a maximal soluble subgroup of the full linear group is completely determined by its irreducible parts and the order in which they occur, it is sufficient to discuss the maximal irreducible subgroups of the full linear group.[1] This discussion in its turn reduces to the study of maximal primitive soluble subgroups of the full linear group, and they will be our main consideration.

We shall now give some results on the structure of maximal primitive soluble subgroups of the full linear group over an arbitrary field.

Let Γ be a maximal primitive soluble subgroup of $\mathrm{GL}(n, P)$,[2] let F be a maximal abelian normal subgroup of Γ, and let V be the centralizer of F in Γ; then the following theorems hold:

1. F is the multiplicative group of a certain field K, $PE_n \subseteq K \subseteq P_n$, $K{:}P$ is a divisor of n.

2. When P is an infinite field, Γ has a unique maximal abelian normal subgroup.

3. V coincides with F if and only if

$$K : P = n.$$

4. Suppose that $K : P = m < n$, and that A/F is maximal among the abelian normal subgroups of Γ/F contained in V/F. Then the normal series $\Gamma \supseteq V \supset A \supset F \supset E$ has the following properties:

(a) A/F is an abelian group of order n^2/m^2 whose primary subgroups are all elementary;

(b) V/A is isomorphic to a soluble subgroup of the automorphism group of A/F;

(c) Γ/V is isomorphic to a certain soluble subgroup of the automorphism group of K relative to P.

5. If $K : P = n$, then Γ/F is isomorphic to a soluble subgroup of the automorphism group of K relative to P.

Now if P is an algebraically closed field or the field of real numbers, then $\mathrm{GL}(n, P)$ contains only a finite number of maximal soluble subgroups that are not conjugate.

---

[1] See Chapter I, §1.
[2] For the notation see below.

If n is an odd number and P the field of real numbers, then a maximal soluble irreducible subgroup of $\mathrm{GL}(n, P)$ is conjugate in $\mathrm{GL}(n, P)$ to a semi-direct product of a certain maximal transitive soluble subgroup of the symmetric group S_n and the complete diagonal subgroup of $\mathrm{GL}(n, P)$.

The maximal soluble irreducible subgroups of $\mathrm{GL}(n, P)$ are completely described in this book in the case when P is an algebraically closed field and n a square-free number. The construction of maximal soluble subgroups of $\mathrm{GL}(n, P)$ for an algebraically closed field P reduces to that of the maximal soluble subgroups of the symplectic groups over finite fields. The case of a finite ground field is treated in detail.

In the study of nilpotent and locally nilpotent linear groups, we confine ourselves to the fundamental case of an algebraically closed ground field. The principal result here is a complete description of the maximal irreducible locally nilpotent subgroups of the full linear group over an algebraically closed field. It turns out that when P is algebraically closed, $\mathrm{GL}(n, P)$ contains to within conjugacy in $\mathrm{GL}(n, P)$ only a single maximal irreducible locally nilpotent subgroup. This statement is analogous to the theorem, which will be proved presently, on the conjugacy of the maximal nilpotent transitive subgroups of the symmetric group.

A number of properties of irreducible nilpotent subgroups of a full linear group will be established. Many of these properties are connected with the theorem that the center of an irreducible nilpotent linear group over an arbitrary field is of finite index.

The study of reducible nilpotent and locally nilpotent linear groups comes down to that of irreducible groups of the same type.[3] Thus we also obtain a complete description of the reducible maximal locally nilpotent subgroups of the full linear group over an algebraically closed field.

Notation and definitions.

1. Let P, K be fields. By $P^{(n)}$, $K^{(n)}$ we denote n-dimensional linear spaces over P, K, and by P_n, K_n the algebras of all linear operators acting on $P^{(n)}$, $K^{(n)}$, respectively.
2. $\mathrm{GL}(n, P)$, $\mathrm{GL}(n, K)$ are full linear groups.
3. A finite field of order p^m will be denoted by the symbol $\mathrm{GF}(p^m)$.
4. If $P = \mathrm{GF}(p^m)$, then we shall sometimes write $\mathrm{GL}(n, p^m)$ instead of $\mathrm{GL}(n, P)$.
5. $\mathrm{SL}(n, P)$ is the special linear group, the group of all elements of $\mathrm{GL}(n, P)$ whose determinants are equal to one.

[3] In contrast to the case of soluble groups, this reduction is not trivial, because a reducible group whose irreducible parts are all nilpotent need not be nilpotent.

6. If a and b are matrices, then $a \times b$ is their Kronecker product.

7. $S_p(2l, P)$ is the symplectic group, the group of all matrices S of order $2l$ over P is subject to the condition:

$$S\Phi S' = \Phi,$$

where

$$\Phi = E_l \times \begin{bmatrix} 0 & 1 \\ -1 & 0 \end{bmatrix}.$$

8. E_n is the unit matrix of order n.

9. If Γ is a group and H a subgroup of it, then $\Gamma : H$ is the index of H in Γ.

If Q is a space over P, then $Q : P$ is the dimension of Q over P. In particular, the rank of the algebra A_0 over P will be denoted by $A_0 : P$.

10. S_n is the symmetric group of degree n.

11. Let Γ be a subgroup of $\mathrm{GL}(n, P)$. If $P^{(n)}$ has an invariant subspace Q relative to Γ, $Q \neq 0$, $Q \neq P^{(n)}$, then Γ is called reducible. But if $P^{(n)}$ only has the trivial invariant subspaces relative to Γ, then Γ is called irreducible.

If $P^{(n)}$ is the direct sum of minimal (irreducible) invariant subspaces relative to Γ, then Γ is called completely reducible.

12. Let Γ be a group, Z_1 the center of Γ, Z_2/Z_1 the center of Γ/Z_1, Z_{j+1}/Z_j the center of Γ/Z_j. If for a finite l we have $Z_l = \Gamma$, then Γ is called nilpotent, the series $E \subset Z_1 \subset Z_2 \subset \cdots \subset Z_l = \Gamma$ is the upper central series of Γ and the number l is the class of nilpotency of Γ.

13. If $H \subset P_n$, then $[H]$ denotes the linear P_n-hull of H.

14. p is a prime number.

CHAPTER I

SOLUBLE GROUPS OF MATRICES OVER AN ARBITRARY FIELD

1. Preliminary lemmas and Clifford's theorem.

1. Let P be an arbitrary field and Γ a subgroup of $GL(n, P)$.

The space $P^{(n)}$ always has a basis in which the matrices A_g of the operators g of Γ can be simultaneously reduced to the form

$$A_g=\begin{bmatrix} A_{11}^g & A_{12}^g & \cdots & A_{1k}^g \\ 0 & A_{22}^g & \cdots & A_{2k}^g \\ \vdots & \vdots & \ddots & \vdots \\ 0 & 0 & \cdots & A_{kk}^g \end{bmatrix}, \tag{1}$$

where the correspondence $g \to A_{ii}^g$ is an irreducible representation Γ_i of degree n_i of Γ, $n_1+n_2+\cdots+n_k=n$ (see [**3**, §110]). It is easy to show that when the groups $\Gamma_1, \Gamma_2, \cdots, \Gamma_k$ are soluble, the whole group Γ is itself soluble. In fact, the mapping

$$g \to \begin{bmatrix} A_{11}^g & 0 & \cdots & 0 \\ 0 & A_{22}^g & \cdots & 0 \\ \vdots & \vdots & \ddots & \vdots \\ 0 & 0 & \cdots & A_{kk}^g \end{bmatrix}$$

is a homomorphism whose kernel consists of the matrices of the form

$$\begin{bmatrix} E_{n_1} & B_{12} & \cdots & B_{1k} \\ 0 & E_{n_2} & \cdots & B_{2k} \\ \vdots & \vdots & \ddots & \vdots \\ 0 & 0 & \cdots & E_{n_k} \end{bmatrix} \tag{2}$$

A group of matrices of the form (2) is always soluble and its derived length does not exceed $k-1$. Therefore, if all the irreducible groups $\Gamma_1, \Gamma_2, \cdots, \Gamma_k$ are soluble, then Γ is also soluble and the derived length of Γ does not exceed the number

$$l+k-1, \tag{3}$$

where l is the maximal length of the derived series of the Γ_i.

We shall call the groups $\Gamma_1, \Gamma_2, \cdots, \Gamma_k$ the *irreducible parts of* Γ. Obviously, a maximal soluble subgroup of $GL(n, P)$ is completely determined by its irreducible parts and the order in which they occur.

2. A subgroup Γ of $GL(n, P)$ is called *imprimitive* if the space $P^{(n)}$ can be represented as the direct sum of k subspaces ($k>1$) that are permuted among each other by the elements of Γ. If such a decomposition of $P^{(n)}$ is impossible, then Γ is called primitive.

Clearly, every subgroup of the full linear group containing a primitive subgroup is itself primitive.

Let Γ be an irreducible imprimitive subgroup of $GL(n, P)$ and

$$P^{(n)}=Q_1\dot{+}Q_2\dot{+}\cdots\dot{+}Q_k \tag{4}$$

a direct sum of subspaces that are carried into one another by the elements of Γ. The subspaces Q_i are called systems of imprimitivity of Γ. Since Γ is irreducible, the elements of Γ permute $Q_1, \cdots, Q_k$ transitively. Obviously, all the elements of Γ that interchange the vectors of Q_i within Q_i form a certain subgroup H_i of Γ, and if $g\in\Gamma$, $g(Q_i)=Q_j$, then $gH_ig^{-1}=H_j$. Let $g_2(Q_1)=Q_2, \cdots, g_k(Q_1)=Q_k$, $g_i\in\Gamma$; then the elements:

$$g_1=e, g_2, \cdots, g_k \tag{5}$$

form a complete system of left coset representatives of H_1 in Γ. For the cosets g_iH_1, g_jH_1 are distinct for $i\neq j$, because $g_iH_1(Q_1)=Q_i$, $g_jH_1(Q_1)=Q_j$. If $g\in\Gamma$, then $g(Q_1)=Q_i$ for a certain i. Therefore, $g_i^{-1}g(Q_1)=Q_1$, $g_i^{-1}g\in H_1$, $g\in g_iH_1$.

LEMMA 1. *H_i induces in Q_i an irreducible subgroup Γ^i of* $GL(n/k, P)$.

PROOF. Let R_1 be a subspace, $0\subset R_1\subset Q_1$, $H_1(R_1)=R_1$. We examine $R=g_1(R_1)+\cdots+g_k(R_1)$ (see (5)), $g(R)=gg_1(R_1)+\cdots+gg_k(R_1)$. Obviously, $gg_1\in g_{i_1}H_1$, $gg_2\in g_{i_2}H_1, \cdots, gg_k\in g_{i_k}H_1$, where $i_1, i_2, \cdots, i_k$ is a permutation of $1, 2, \cdots, k$. Therefore, $g(R)=(R)$. This contradicts the irreducibility of Γ. The lemma is now proved.

If Γ^1 (see Lemma 1) is imprimitive and $Q_{11}, \cdots, Q_{1l}$ are systems of imprimitivity of Γ^1, $(Q_1=Q_{11}+\cdots+Q_{1l})$, then $P^{(n)}$ can be represented as the direct sum of the kl systems of imprimitivity of $\Gamma: Q_{11}, \cdots, Q_{1l}; \cdots; Q_{k1}=g_k(Q_{11}), \cdots, Q_{kl}=g_k(Q_{1l})$. For suppose that $g\in\Gamma$. Then $g(Q_{ij})=gg_i(Q_{1j})=g_\nu h_1(Q_{1j})$, where $h_1\in H_1$. Therefore, $g(Q_{ij})=g_\nu(Q_{1\mu})=Q_{\nu\mu}$. From this remark we deduce

LEMMA 2. *For an irreducible subgroup Γ of* $GL(n, P)$, *there exists a decom-*

position of the space $P^{(n)}$ into a direct sum of the form (4) *such that the groups Γ^i determined by this decomposition are primitive* (*see Lemma* 1).

A decomposition of $P^{(n)}$ as in Lemma 2 is called a *complete* decomposition of $P^{(n)}$ into systems of imprimitivity of Γ.

3. Now let Γ be a maximal soluble irreducible subgroup of $\mathrm{GL}(n, P)$. Two cases are possible: (a) Γ is primitive, (b) Γ is imprimitive. Later we shall show that the case (b) can be reduced in a certain sense to (a).

Suppose that (b) holds and that a complete decomposition of $P^{(n)}$ into systems of imprimitivity of Γ can be written in the form:

$$P^{(n)} = Q_1 \dot{+} Q_2 \dot{+} \cdots \dot{+} Q_k. \tag{6}$$

By Lemmas 1 and 2, the subgroup H_i induces in Q_i an irreducible primitive group $\Gamma^i \subseteq \mathrm{GL}(n/k, P)$. Now we construct a group $G_i \subset \mathrm{GL}(n, P)$ with the two properties: (1) the elements of G_i leave the vectors of the subspaces Q_j, $i \neq j$, fixed; (2) G_i acts on the subspace Q_i like the group H_i. Obviously, $G_i \cong \Gamma^i$. It is easy to see that the product of the k groups $G_1 G_2 \cdots G_k = G$ is direct.

LEMMA 3. *Γ contains the direct product $G = G_1 \cdots G_k$ as a normal subgroup.*

In fact, for $g \in \Gamma$, $gH_i g^{-1} = H_j$. By the properties of the G_i we have $gG_i g^{-1} = G_j$. Therefore, $gGg^{-1} = G$. Hence, it follows that the group $\Gamma G = G\Gamma \supseteq \Gamma$ is soluble. The maximality of Γ implies that $\Gamma G = \Gamma$, $G \subset \Gamma$.

LEMMA 4. *Γ^i is a maximal soluble subgroup of* $\mathrm{GL}(n/k, P)$.

PROOF. Suppose that $\Gamma^1 \subset K^1$, where K^1 is a soluble subgroup of $\mathrm{GL}(n/k, P)$. We construct a group $K_1 \subset \mathrm{GL}(n, P)$ whose elements leave the vectors of the subspaces $Q_2, \cdots, Q_k$ fixed and act in Q_1 like the elements of K^1. Obviously, $K_1 \supset G_1$. We now consider $gK_1 g^{-1}$, where $g \in \Gamma$. We can write g in the form $g = g_i h_1$, where $h_1 \in H_1$ (see (5)). Therefore, $gK_1 g^{-1} = g_i h_1 K_1 h_1^{-1} g_i^{-1} = g_i K_1 g_i^{-1} = K_i$. Hence, $gK_1 K_2 \cdots K_k g^{-1} = K_1 K_2 \cdots K_k = K$. Thus, the group $\Gamma K = K\Gamma$ is soluble. But $\Gamma K \subset \Gamma$, and this contradicts the maximality of Γ. The lemma is proved.

Thus, Γ^i is a maximal irreducible primitive soluble subgroup of $\mathrm{GL}(n/k, P)$.

Now let $u_{11}, u_{12}, \cdots, u_{1l}$ be a basis of the subspace Q_1 in (6). As a basis of the subspaces Q_ν we choose the vectors

$$u_{\nu 1} = g_\nu(u_{11}),\quad u_{\nu 2} = g_\nu(u_{12}), \cdots, u_{\nu l} = g_\nu(u_{1l}), \tag{7}$$

where g belongs to the system (5).

The vectors $u_{11}, \cdots, u_{1l}; \cdots; u_{k1}, \cdots, u_{kl}$ obviously form a basis of $P^{(n)}$. Observe that for this choice of a basis of $P^{(n)}$ the group G (see Lemma 3) induces in the subspaces $Q_1, \cdots, Q_k$ one and the same group of matrices of degree n/k.

For let a_1 range over G_1 (see Lemma 3) and

$$a_1(u_{1i}) = \sum_{j=1}^{l} \alpha_{ji} u_{1j}, \quad i = 1, \cdots, l, \quad \alpha_{ij} \in P.$$

Then $a_\nu = g_\nu a_1 g_\nu^{-1}$ ranges over G_ν and

$$a_\nu(u_{\nu i}) = g_\nu a_1 g_\nu^{-1} g_\nu(u_{1i}) = g_\nu a_1(u_{1i}) = g_\nu(\sum_{j=1}^{l} \alpha_{ji}\ u_{1j}) = \sum_{j=1}^{l} \alpha_{ji}\ u_{\nu j}.$$

The truth of our remark follows from this.

LEMMA 5. *The group Γ can be represented as a semidirect product*

$$\Gamma = TG, \tag{8}$$

where the subgroup T is isomorphic to a certain maximal soluble transitive subgroup of the symmetric group S_k and consists of elements t of the form

$$t(u_{\nu\mu}) = u_{i_\nu \mu}, \quad \nu = 1, \cdots, k; \ \mu = 1, \cdots, l, \tag{9}$$

where $i_1, \cdots, i_k$ is a permutation of $1, \cdots, k$, and the normal subgroup G of Γ is defined in Lemma 3.

PROOF. Let $g \in \Gamma$. We examine $g(u_{\nu\mu})$, $\nu = 1, \cdots, k$, $\mu = 1, \cdots, l$ (see (7)). We have

$$g(u_{\nu\mu}) = g g_\nu(u_{1\mu}) = g_{i_\nu} h_{1\nu}(u_{1\mu}) = g_{i_\nu} a_{1\nu}(u_{1\mu}),$$

where $h_{1\nu} \in H_1$, $a_{1\nu} \in G_1$.

$$g_{i_\nu} a_{1\nu}(u_{1\mu}) = g_{i_\nu}(\sum_{j=1}^{l} \alpha_{j\mu}^{\nu} u_{1j}) = g_{i_\nu} g_\nu^{-1}(\sum_{j=1}^{l} \alpha_{j\mu}^{\nu} u_{\nu j})$$

$$\nu = 1, \cdots, k, \quad \mu = 1, \cdots, l.$$

By Lemma 3 and the remark made after (7) the matrices of the elements of G assume in the basis $u_{\nu\mu}$ the form:

$$\begin{bmatrix} A_1 & 0 & \cdots & 0 \\ 0 & A_2 & \cdots & 0 \\ \vdots & \vdots & \vdots & \vdots \\ 0 & 0 & \cdots & A_k \end{bmatrix}, \tag{10}$$

where $A_1, \cdots, A_k$ independently range over one and the same group of matrices of degree n/k.

Therefore, G contains an element a such that

$$a(u_{\nu\mu}) = \sum_{j=1}^{l} \alpha^{\nu}_{j\mu} u_{\nu j}, \quad \nu = 1, \cdots, k; \quad \mu = 1, \cdots, l.$$

We set

$$a^{-1}(u_{\nu\mu}) = \sum_{j=1}^{l} \beta^{\nu}_{j\mu} u_{\nu j}, \quad \nu = 1, \cdots, k, \quad \mu = 1, \cdots, l,$$

and consider the element $ga^{-1} \in \Gamma$.

$$ga^{-1}(u_{\nu\mu}) = g(\sum_{j=1}^{l} \beta^{\nu}_{j\mu} u_{\nu j}) = gg_{\nu}(\sum_{j=1}^{l} \beta^{\nu}_{j\mu} u_{1j})$$

$$= g_{i_\nu} h_{1\nu}(\sum_{j=1}^{l} \beta^{\nu}_{j\mu} u_{1j}) = g_{i_\nu} a_{1\nu}(\sum_{j=1}^{l} \beta^{\nu}_{j\mu} u_{1j}) = g_{i_\nu}(u_{1\mu}) = u_{i_\nu \mu}.$$

Therefore, $ga^{-1}(u_{\nu\mu}) = u_{i_\nu \mu}$, $\nu = 1, \cdots, k$, $\mu = 1, \cdots, l$,

$$ga^{-1} = t \ \text{(see (9))}, \quad g = ta, \quad \Gamma = TG.$$

The lemma is proved.

Thus, if a maximal irreducible soluble subgroup of $\mathrm{GL}(n, P)$ is imprimitive, then it is completely determined by a certain maximal soluble irreducible primitive subgroup of $\mathrm{GL}(n/k, P)$ and a maximal transitive soluble subgroup of S_k, where k is the number of systems of imprimitivity of the complete decomposition of $P^{(n)}$ into systems of imprimitivity of Γ.

It is easy to see that every soluble irreducible subgroup of $\mathrm{GL}(n, P)$ for which the complete decomposition of $P^{(n)}$ coincides with (6) is contained in the group

$$\Gamma' = T'G', \tag{8a}$$

where T' is isomorphic to a subgroup of a symmetric group and the normal subgroup G' is isomorphic to a direct product of k copies of a primitive soluble subgroup of $\mathrm{GL}(n/k, P)$.

4. We shall frequently use a theorem of Clifford. Later we give a simple proof of this theorem that is based on elementary properties of additive operator groups.

CLIFFORD'S THEOREM [11]. *Let Γ be an irreducible subgroup of* $\mathrm{GL}(n, P)$ *and H a normal subgroup of Γ. Then*: 1. *The space $P^{(n)}$ can be represented as a direct sum of subspaces $L_1, \cdots, L_s$ of one and the same dimension that are invariant and irreducible relative to H.* 2. *If L_j is regarded as an additive* *operator group (the operator domain consisting of the elements of P and H), then the direct sums of the operator isomorphic subspaces L_j are systems of imprimitivity of Γ. In particular, if Γ is primitive, then all the L_j are operator isomorphic to each other.*

COROLLARY. *The linear P-hull $[H]$ of a normal subgroup H of an irreducible primitive group Γ is a simple algebra over P.*

PROOF OF CLIFFORD'S THEOREM [**23**]. Let L_1 be a subspace of $P^{(n)}$ that is invariant and irreducible relative to H. If $b_2 \in \Gamma$, then $Hb_2(L_1) = b_2Hb_2^{-1}b_2(L_1) = b_2(L_1)$. $L_1 + b_2(L_1)$ either coincides with L_1 or is the direct sum of two subspaces that are invariant and irreducible relative to H. Suppose that $L = L_1 + b_2(L_1) + \cdots + b_s(L_1)$ $b_j \in \Gamma$, is a direct sum such that for every $g \in \Gamma$ the sum $L + g(L_1)$ is no longer direct. Then $g(L_1) \subset L$, $g(L) = L$,

$$L = L_1 + L_2 + \cdots + L_s = P^{(n)}, \tag{11}$$

where $L_j = b_j(L_1)$. This proves the first part of the theorem.

Now let Q_1 be the direct sum of all subspaces L_j in (11) that are operator isomorphic to L_1. If $R \subset P^{(n)}$ and $R \cong L_1$, then $R \subset Q_1$, because every decomposition of $P^{(n)}$ into a direct sum of minimal admissible subgroups contains as many terms isomorphic to L_1 as there are in (11). We also note that if $R_1 \subset P^{(n)}$, $R_2 \subset P^{(n)}$ and $R_1 \cong R_2$, then $g(R_1) \cong g(R_2)$ for every g of Γ. For suppose that $r_1 \to r_2$, $hr_1 \to hr_2$, $r_1 \in R_1$, $r_2 \in R_2$, $h \in H$. Now if $g(r_1) \to g(r_2)$, then $hg(r_1) = gh_1(r_1) \to gh_1(r_2) = hg(r_2)$. Consequently, $g(R_1)$ is operator isomorphic to $g(R_2)$.

We now examine $g(Q_1)$, where $g \in \Gamma$. $g(Q_1)$ contains $g(L_1)$ as a direct summand, and all the other summands of $g(Q_1)$ are isomorphic to $g(L_1)$. In (11) we can find terms L_i such that $g(L_1) \cong L_i$. Therefore, $g(Q_1)$ is contained in the direct sum Q_2 of all the subspaces L_j in (11) that are isomorphic to $L_i g(Q_1) \subseteq Q_2$. However, $g^{-1}(L_i) \cong L_1$. Consequently, $g^{-1}(Q_2) \subseteq Q_1$. Hence, $g(Q_1) = Q_2$. The proof of the theorem is now complete.

5. Next we shall prove a lemma on central subalgebras of P_n, which will be required later.

Let A_0 be a subalgebra of P_n. If the center of A_0 coincides with PE_n, then A_0 is called a central subalgebra of P_n.

LEMMA 6. *Let $A_0 \neq P_n$ be a central irreducible subalgebra of P_n. Then in $\mathrm{GL}(n, P) \setminus A_0$ there are matrices that are permutable with every matrix of A_0.*

PROOF. Since A_0 is irreducible, it is simple. Thus A_0 is a complete matrix ring D_t over a certain field D. Then $A_0 = D_t$, $A_0 : P = t^2(D : P) = t^2 m$, $n = tm$, $t < n$, $m > 1$. The center of D coincides with PE_m. The centralizer of D_t in P_n consists of all the matrices of the form $E_t \times d'$, $d' \in D'$, where D' is the field that is inversely isomorphic to D. $D' \cap D = PE_m$,

$$E_t \times d' \in \mathrm{GL}(n, P) \setminus A_0$$

if $d' \notin PE_m$. This proves the lemma (see [**5**, p. 90]).

2. **Abelian normal subgroups of primitive soluble subgroups of** GL(n, P).
1. Throughout what follows we shall apply the concept of primitivity (and imprimitivity) of a linear group only to *irreducible* subgroups of GL(n, P).

We begin the study of primitive soluble subgroups of GL(n, P) by clarifying the structure of their abelian normal subgroups.

LEMMA 7. *Let* Γ *be a primitive soluble subgroup of* GL(n,P) *and* H *an abelian normal subgroup of* Γ. *Then* H *is a subgroup of the multiplicative group of a certain field* K *contained in the algebra* P_n *whose degree* $K : P$ *is a divisor of* n.

PROOF. We consider the linear P-hull $[H]$ of H. Since H is a normal subgroup of a primitive group, Clifford's theorem is applicable to $[H]$ (see the corollary). Thus $[H]$ is a simple commutative subalgebra of P_n. Therefore $K = [H]$ is a field. Furthermore, $P^{(n)}$ is the direct sum of subspaces invariant and irreducible relative to K:

$$P^{(n)} = Q_1 \dotplus \cdots \dotplus Q_s, \quad Q_i : P = n/s. \tag{12}$$

If $q_i \in Q_i$, $q_i \neq 0$, then in virtue of the irreducibility of Q_i, $Kq_i = Q_i$. Therefore, $K : P = Q_i : P = n/s$. This proves the lemma.

Now let F be the multiplicative group of the field $K = [H]$. Then $gFg^{-1} = F$ for every $g \in \Gamma$. Therefore $\Gamma F = F\Gamma$ is a soluble group and F an abelian normal subgroup of it. Hence follows

THEOREM 1. *A maximal abelian normal subgroup of a maximal soluble primitive subgroup of* GL(n, P) *is the multiplicative group of a certain field* K *contained in* P_n *whose degree* $K : P$ *divides* n.

For if Γ is a maximal soluble subgroup of GL(n, P), then $F\Gamma = \Gamma$, $H \subseteq F \subset \Gamma$. Now if H is a maximal abelian normal subgroup of Γ, then $H \supseteq F$. Therefore $H = F$. This proves the theorem.

LEMMA 8. *Let* Γ *be a primitive soluble subgroup of* $\mathrm{GL}(n, P)$ *and* H *an abelian normal subgroup of* Γ. *Then* $\mathrm{GL}(n, P)$ *contains a soluble subgroup* $G \supseteq \Gamma$ *with a maximal abelian normal subgroup* F *that contains* H *and is the multiplicative group of a certain field* $K \subset P_n$, *where* $K:P$ *divides* n.

PROOF. $\Gamma \subseteq G_1 = \Gamma F_1$, where F_1 is the multiplicative group of the field $K_1 = [H]$. If F_1 is a maximal abelian normal subgroup of G_1, then the lemma is proved. But if $F_1 \subset H_1$, where H_1 is an abelian normal subgroup of G_1, then we consider the group $G_2 = G_1 F_2$, where F_2 is the multiplicative group of the field $K_2 = [H_1]$. Obviously, $K_1 \subset K_2$. Continuing in this way we obtain a series of fields $K_1 \subset K_2 \subset \cdots$. Since $K_j : P$ is a divisor of n, this series must be finite. Therefore, after a finite number of steps we arrive at the required soluble group G.

2. Now let G be an irreducible soluble subgroup of $\mathrm{GL}(n, P)$ with a maximal abelian normal subgroup F that is the multiplicative group of a certain field $K \subset P_n$, $K : P = m$, m/n.

Let V be the centralizer of F in G.

THEOREM 2. *The factor-group* G/V *is isomorphic to a certain soluble subgroup of the group of automorphisms of* K *relative to* PE_n.

PROOF. Suppose that $g \in G$, $x, y \in K$; then $gxg^{-1} \in K$, $g(x+y)g^{-1} = gxg^{-1} + gyg^{-1}$, $g(xy)g^{-1} = gxg^{-1}gyg^{-1}$, $g\lambda E_n g^{-1} = \lambda E_n$ for $\lambda \in P$. Thus, the mapping $x \to gxg^{-1} = \sigma(x)$ is an automorphism of K. The correspondence $g \to \sigma$ is a homomorphism of G into the automorphism group of K relative to PE_n. Since $K = [F]$, the kernel of this homomorphism coincides with V. Hence the theorem follows.

COROLLARY.

$$G : V \leqq K : P = m. \tag{13}$$

The n-dimensional space $P^{(n)}$ over P can be regarded as a (n/m)-dimensional space over K. For $P^{(n)}$ can be written in the form (see (12) and below)

$$P^{(n)} = Q_1 \dotplus \cdots \dotplus Q_r = Kq_1 \dotplus \cdots \dotplus Kq_r,$$

where $r = n/m$.

If $\alpha_1, \alpha_2, \cdots, \alpha_r$ are elements of K, then $\alpha_1 q_1 + \alpha_2 q_2 + \cdots + \alpha_r q_r$ vanishes only when $\alpha_1 = \alpha_2 = \cdots = \alpha_r = 0$. Therefore $P^{(n)} = K^{(r)}$.

Such a representation of $P^{(n)}$ is convenient for the study of V. It is easy to work out that V is a subgroup of $\mathrm{GL}(r, K)$. For if $x, y \in K^{(r)}$, and $\alpha \in K$, then for every $v \in V$ we have $v(x+y)=v(x)+v(y)$, $v(\alpha x)=\alpha v(x)$, since every element of V permutes with every element of K. So $V \subseteq \mathrm{GL}(r, K)$.

Obviously, $\mathrm{GL}(r, K)$ is the centralizer of F in $\mathrm{GL}(n, P)$. If $K:P=n$, then $V \subseteq \mathrm{GL}(1, K)=F$. Consequently, for $K:P=n$ we have $V=F$. Later we shall see that the converse statement also holds: If $V=F$, then $K:P=n$ (see Theorem 10).

3. We shall now assume that $V \neq F$. We examine the factor group G/F. G/F has nontrivial abelian normal subgroups contained in V/F. Such a normal subgroup is, for example, the penultimate term of the derived series of V/F. Let A/F be a nontrivial abelian normal subgroup of G/F and of V/F. Obviously, the center of A contains F, hence the maximality of F implies that A coincides with F.

LEMMA 9. *The order of every element of the factor-group A/F is a divisor of the number $r=n/m$. If aF is an element of A/F of order ν, then A contains an element b such that the commutator $(a,b)=aba^{-1}b^{-1}$ is of order ν.*

PROOF. For arbitrary elements a and b of A we have $ab=fba$, where $f \in F$, $a^k b=f^k b a^k$. The determinants of the elements ab and fba of $\mathrm{GL}(r, K)$ coincide. Therefore, $f^r=1$, $a^r b=ba^r$, $a^r \in F$, $(aF)^r=F$. The order of aF divides r. Now suppose that the order of aF is equal to ν. If $c \in A$, $d \in A$, then $(a,c)\,(a,d)=(a,cd)$.

On the other hand, all the (a,c) are elements of K, and $(a,c)^r=1$. Hence, it follows that all the commutators of the form (a,c) form a finite cyclic group. Let it be of order τ. Then $(a^\tau, c)=(a,c)^\tau=1$. Therefore ν/τ. But $(a,c)^\nu=(a^\nu,c)=1$ so that τ/ν. Hence $\tau=\nu$. This proves the lemma.

LEMMA 10. $A:F=[A]:K$.

PROOF. If $c_1, c_2, \cdots, c_k$ are elements of A, linearly independent over K, then they obviously belong to distinct cosets of F in A. Now let $d_1, d_2, \cdots, d_\rho$ be representatives of ρ distinct cosets of F in A. We shall show that they are linearly independent over K. For every $a \in A$ we have $ad_j a^{-1}= f_j d_j$, where $f_j \in F$; also for $i \neq j$ we can find a in A such that $f_j \neq f_i$. For suppose that for every a of A we have $f_i=f_j$, i.e., $f_i=ad_i a^{-1}d_i^{-1}=f_j= ad_j a_j^{-1} d_j^{-1}$. Then $(a, d_j^{-1}d_i)=1$, $d_j^{-1}d_i \in F$, $d_i \in d_j F$. This contradicts the choice of the elements $d_1, d_2, \cdots, d_\rho$.

Now suppose that $d_1, d_2, \cdots, d_\rho$ are linearly dependent over K. Of all the nontrivial linear relations connecting $d_1, d_2, \cdots, d_\rho$ we choose one that contains the least number of nonzero terms:

$$\lambda_1 d_1+\lambda_2 d_2+\cdots+\lambda_\rho d_\rho=0, \qquad \lambda_i\in K. \tag{15}$$

We may assume that $\lambda_1\neq 0$, $\lambda_2\neq 0$. In A we choose a such that $ad_1a^{-1}d_1^{-1}=f_1\neq ad_2a^{-1}d_2^{-1}=f_2$. Then

$$f_1(\lambda_1 d_1+\lambda_2 d_2+\cdots+\lambda_\rho d_\rho)-a(\lambda_1 d_1+\lambda_2 d_2+\cdots+\lambda_\rho d_\rho)a^{-1}$$
$$=\lambda_2(f_1-f_2)d_2+\cdots+\lambda_\rho(f_1-f_\rho)d_\rho=0, \qquad \lambda_2(f_1-f_2)\neq 0.$$

The last equation contradicts the choice of the relation (15).

Now it is easy to prove the lemma. Let $u_1, u_2,\cdots, u_k$ be a maximal system of elements of A that are linearly independent over K. Then the system is on the one hand a K-basis of $[A]$, and on the other hand, a complete set of coset representatives of F in A. The lemma now follows. Since $A\subset \mathrm{GL}(r, K)$ and $[A]\subset K_r$, we have

$$A:F=[A]:K\leqq r^2=n^2/m^2. \tag{16}$$

THEOREM 3. *In A we can choose elements $a_1, b_1, a_2, b_2,\cdots, a_t, b_t$, such that* (i) $(a_i, b_i)=a_ib_ia_i^{-1}b_i^{-1}=\epsilon_i$, *where ϵ_i is an element of F of order ν_i and ν_{i+1} divides ν_i*; (ii) *the elements belonging to distinct pairs are permutable*; (iii) *every element a of A has a unique representation in the form*

$$a=f\,a_1^{\alpha_1}b_1^{\beta_1}\cdots a_t^{\alpha_t}b_t^{\beta_t} \qquad f\in F, \quad 0\leqq \alpha_i, \quad \beta_i<\nu_i. \tag{17}$$

PROOF. Let ν_1 be the smallest among the order of the elements of A/F. Then A contains a pair of elements a_1, b_1 such that $(a_1, b_1)=\epsilon_1$, where ϵ_1 is an element of F of order ν_1 (see Lemma 9). The group A can be written in the form $A=(a_1)(b_1)A_1$, where A_1 is the centralizer on the elements a_1 and b_1 in A. In fact, there are ν_1 elements conjugate to a_1 in A. There are just as many elements conjugate to b_1. Hence $A:A_1\leqq \nu_1^2$. On the other hand, all elements of the form $a_1^{\alpha_1}b_1^{\beta_1}$, $0\leqq \alpha_1$, $\beta_1<\nu_1$ belong to distinct cosets of A_1 in A, because $(a_1^{\alpha_1}b_1^{\beta_1}, b_1)=\epsilon_1^{\alpha_1}$, $(a_1, a_1^{\alpha_1}b_1^{\beta_1})=\epsilon_1^{\beta_1}$. Consequently,

$$A:A_1=\nu^2 \qquad \text{and} \qquad A=(a_1)(b_1)A_1. \tag{18}$$

If A_1 is an abelian group, then $A_1=F$, $A=(a_1)(b_1)F$ and the theorem is proved.

Suppose that $A_1\neq F$ and that ν_2 is the smallest among the orders of the elements of the factor-group A_1/F. Obviously, ν_2/ν_1. By Lemma 9 and equation (18), A_1 contains a pair of elements a_2, b_2 such that $(a_2, b_2)=\epsilon_2$ where ϵ_2 is an element of F of order ν_2. Thus, $A_1=(a_2)(b_2)A_2$, where A_2 is the centralizer of the elements a_1, b_1, a_2, b_2 in A. $A=(a_1)(b_1)(a_2)(b_2)A_2$, and the elements $a_1^{\alpha_1}b_1^{\beta_1}a_2^{\alpha_2}b_2^{\beta_2}$, $0\leqq\alpha_i$, $\beta_i<\nu_i$, $i=1, 2$, lie in distinct cosets of A_2 in A.

Since A/F is a finite group, after a finite number of steps we arrive at an equation $A=(a_1)(b_1)\cdots(a_t)(b_t)F$, where the elements $a_1^{\alpha_1}b_1^{\beta_1}\cdots a_t^{\alpha_t}b_t^{\beta_t}$, $0\leqq\alpha_i,\ \beta_i<\nu_i$, $i=1,2,\cdots,t$, lie in distinct cosets of A in F. This proves the theorem.

COROLLARY.

$$A:F=\nu_1^2\nu_2^2\cdots\nu_t^2\leqq r^2. \tag{19}$$

4. So far we have assumed that A/F is an arbitrary nontrivial abelian normal subgroup of G/F and V/F. Now we shall assume that A/F is maximal among the abelian normal subgroups of G/F contained in V/F.

THEOREM 4. *Let A/F be maximal among the abelian normal subgroups of G/F contained in V/F. Then A/F coincides with its centralizer in V/F.*

PROOF. From Theorem 3, it follows that

$$A=(a_1)(b_1)(a_2)\cdots(a_t)(b_t)F,\quad (a_i,b_i)=\epsilon_i,\quad (a_i,a_j)=(a_i,b_j)$$
$$=(b_i,b_j)=1,\quad i\neq j,\quad (a_iF)^{\nu_i}=(b_iF)^{\nu_i}=F.$$

Let B/F be the centralizer of A/F and V/F and C the centralizer of A in V. Obviously, $B\supset C\supseteq F$. Now we shall show that $B=AC$. For $b\in B$ we have $(a_i,b)\in F$. Hence, $(a_i^{\nu_i},b)=(a_i,b)^{\nu_i}=1$. Consequently, $(a_i,b)=\epsilon_i^{\beta_i}$, $(b,b_i)=\epsilon_i^{\alpha_i}$, $i=1,2,\cdots,t$.

On the other hand, the element $a=a_1^{\alpha_1}b_1^{\beta_1}\cdots a_t^{\alpha_t}b_t^{\beta_t}$ satisfies the conditions: $(a_i,a)=\epsilon_i^{\beta_i}$, $(a,b_i)=\epsilon_i^{\alpha_i}$, i.e.,

$$(a_i,b)=(a_i,a)=(b,b_i)=(a,b_i).$$

Hence $(a_i,a^{-1}b)=(a^{-1}b,b_i)=1$, $i=1,\cdots,t$.

Therefore

$$a^{-1}b\in C,\ B=AC. \tag{20}$$

Suppose that $B/F\supset A/F$. Then the second-to-the-last term D/A in the derived series of B/A is nontrivial. D/A is an abelian group, but D/F by the maximality of A/F cannot be abelian. Therefore, D contains elements d,d_1 such that

$$(d_1,d)\notin F. \tag{21}$$

By (20), $d=ac$, $d_1=a_1c_1$, $a,a_1\in A$, c, $c_1\in C$. Hence, $(d,d_1)=(ac,a_1c_1)=(a,a_1)\ (c,c_1)\in C$.

Since $(d,d_1)\in A$, we have $(d,d_1)\in C\cap A=F$. This contradicts (21) and proves the theorem.

COROLLARY. *The centralizer of A in G is equal to F.*

3. **Finiteness of the index of a maximal abelian normal subgroup.** Suppose, as before, that G is an irreducible soluble subgroup of $\mathrm{GL}(n, P)$ whose maximal abelian normal subgroup F coincides with the multiplicative group of the field $K \subset P_n$, $K : P = m$, m/n.

THEOREM 5.

$$G : F \leqq \rho(n) = n^2(n^2-1)(n^2-2)(n^2-2^2)\cdots(n^2-2^{l-1}), \tag{22}$$

where $l = [2\log_2 n]$.

PROOF. We distinguish two cases: (i) F coincides with its centralizer V in G; (ii) $F \neq V$.

In case (i), on the basis of Theorem 2, we obtain

$$G : F = G : V \leqq K : P = m \leqq n < \rho(n).$$

Now suppose that $F \neq V$ and that A/F is maximal among the abelian normal subgroups of G/F contained in V/F. Obviously,

$$G : F = (G : V)(V : A)(A : F). \tag{23}$$

By (13) and (16) we have $G : V \leqq m$, $A : F \leqq n^2/m^2$; it remains to estimate $V : A$.

Obviously, $V : A = V/F : A/F$. Since A/F coincides with its centralizer in V/F (see Theorem 4), the factor-group $(V/F)/(A/F)$ is isomorphic to a certain soluble subgroup of the automorphism group of the finite abelian group A/F. The order of A/F does not exceed the number $r^2 = n^2/m^2$. Consequently, the order of its automorphism group cannot be greater than $(r^2-1)(r^2-2)\cdots(r^2-2^{k-1})$, where $k = [2\log_2 r]$. From this and from (23) we obtain: $G : F \leqq (n^2/m)(r^2-1)(r^2-2)\cdots(r^2-2^{k-1}) \leqq n^2(n^2-1)\cdots(n^2-2^{l-1})$, where $l = [2\log_2 n]$. The theorem is now proved.

From it we derive

THEOREM 6. *Every primitive soluble subgroup of* $\mathrm{GL}(n, P)$ *has an abelian normal subgroup whose index does not exceed* $\rho(n)$ *(see* (22)).

For suppose that Γ is a primitive soluble subgroup of $\mathrm{GL}(n, P)$ and H an abelian normal subgroup of it. Then, by Lemma 8, $\Gamma \subseteq G$, $H \subseteq F$. Furthermore, $\Gamma : H \cap F = \Gamma F : F \leqq G : F \leqq \rho(n)$.

Later on we shall require the following obvious

LEMMA 11. *Let Ω be an infinite field and Δ a subfield of Ω. If the index of the* *multiplicative group of* Δ *in the multiplicative group of* Ω *is finite, then* $\Omega=\Delta$.

THEOREM 7. *A maximal primitive soluble subgroup of* $\mathrm{GL}(n, P)$ *in the case of an infinite ground field* P *has a unique maximal abelian normal subgroup.*

PROOF. We shall prove a slightly different statement from which Theorem 7 can be simply derived. Let G be a soluble irreducible subgroup of $\mathrm{GL}(n, P)$ (where P is an infinite field), let F and F' be maximal abelian normal subgroups of G such that F is the multiplicative group of a field $K\subset P_n$, and let F' be the multiplicative group of a field $K'\subset P_n$. Then $F'=F$.

For by (22), $F:(F\cap F')=FF':F'\leqq G:F'\leqq\rho(n)$. Obviously, $F\cap F'$ is the multiplicative group of the field $K\cap K'$. By Lemma 11, $K\cap K'=K$, $K'\supseteq K$, $F'\supseteq F$, $F'=F$.

Theorem 7 follows from the statement proved and Theorem 1.

THEOREM 8 (ZASSENHAUS). *Every primitive soluble subgroup of* $\mathrm{GL}(n, P)$ *is contained in a maximal soluble subgroup of* $\mathrm{GL}(n, P)$.

PROOF. Since for a finite ground field P the theorem is obvious, we shall assume that P is infinite. Let Γ be a primitive soluble subgroup of $\mathrm{GL}(n, P)$. By Lemma 8, Γ is contained in a soluble group $G\subset\mathrm{GL}(n, P)$ having a maximal abelian normal subgroup F such that F is the multiplicative group of a certain field $K\subset P_n$, $K:P=m$, m/n.

Let $M_0(\Gamma)$ be the set of all such groups G containing Γ. Since $K:P\leqq n$, we can select in M_0 the subset M_{01} consisting of all those $G\in M_0(\Gamma)$ for which the degree $K:P$ is maximal.

Furthermore, $G:F\leqq\rho(n)$; consequently, in M_{01}, in its turn, we can select the subset M_{02} consisting of all those $G\in M_{01}$ for which the index $G:F$ is maximal. We shall now show that every group in M_{02} is a maximal soluble subgroup of $\mathrm{GL}(n, P)$. Suppose that $G\in M_{02}$ and that $G\subset\Gamma'$, where Γ' is a soluble subgroup of $\mathrm{GL}(n, P)$. By Lemma 8, $\Gamma'\leqq G'\in M_0$. Suppose that the multiplicative group F' of K' is a maximal abelian normal subgroup of G'. Then $F:(F\cap F')=FF':F'\leqq G':F'\leqq\rho(n)$. By Lemma 11, $K\cap K'=K$, $K'\supseteq K$. But from the construction of M_{01} it follows that $K:P\geqq K':P$. Therefore, $K'=K$, $F'=F$. Moreover, from the properties of M_{02} it follows that $G:F\geqq G':F$. The latter contradicts the inclusion $G\subset G'$, and the theorem is proved.

Note that the following more general theorem holds: Every soluble subgroup of $\mathrm{GL}(n, P)$ is contained in a maximal soluble subgroup of $\mathrm{GL}(n, P)$ (Zassenhaus). We shall not prove this here.

4. **The factor-group** A/F.

1. Now let G be a maximal primitive soluble subgroup of $\mathrm{GL}(n, P)$, let F be a maximal abelian normal subgroup of G, let $K \subset P_n$ be a field whose multiplicative group coincides with F, and let V be the centralizer of F in G, with A/F maximal among the abelian normal subgroups of G/F contained in V/F. We shall show that the order of the factor-group A/F is equal to n^2/m^2, where $m = K : P$. We shall show, furthermore, that to within isomorphism the factor-group A/F is uniquely determined by the number n/m. Although for $V = F$ the group A coincides with F and is not needed in the investigation, nevertheless, the formula $A : F = n^2/m^2$ gives, even in this case, a nontrivial result: F coincides with its centralizer in G if and only if $K : P = n$.

LEMMA 12. *The linear P-hull* $[A]$ *of* A *is a simple central algebra over* K.

We observe, first of all, that the P-hull of A coincides with the K-hull of the same group, because $A \supset F$. A is a normal subgroup of G, so that by Clifford's theorem the P-hull of A is a simple algebra over P. We now have to show that the center of $[A]$ coincides with K. We represent every nonzero element of $[A]$ in the form $c = f_1c_1 + f_2c_2 + \cdots + f_kc_k$, where $f_i \in F$ and the c_i are elements of A belonging to distinct cosets of F in A.

Now suppose that c is contained in the center of $[A]$; then for every $a \in A$ we have $c - aca^{-1} = 0$, $ac_ia^{-1} = \lambda_i c_i$, $\lambda_i \in F$. Hence, $f_1(1-\lambda_1)c_1 + f_2(1-\lambda_2)c_2 + \cdots + f_k(1-\lambda_k)c_k = 0$. Since $c_1, \cdots, c_k$ are linearly independent over K, we have $f_i(1-\lambda_i) = 0$, $\lambda_i = 1$.

Since a is an arbitrary element of A and the center of A coincides with F, we have $k = 1$, $c = f_1 \cdot c_1 \in F$. The lemma is now proved.

LEMMA 13. $[A]$ *coincides with the linear P-hull* $[V]$ *of* V.

PROOF. If $v \in V$, then the correspondence

$$x \to v^{-1}xv \tag{24}$$

is an automorphism of A.

From Theorem 4 it follows that the centralizer of A in V coincides with F. Therefore, the elements of V that induce one and the same automorphism (24) lie in the same residue class of F. Since V and $[A]$ are contained in K_r, every automorphism (24) of A can be extended to an automorphism

$$z \to v^{-1}zv, \qquad z \in [A] \tag{25}$$

of the algebra $[A]$ that leaves the elements of its center K fixed. Since $[A]$ is a simple central algebra over K, all such automorphisms are inner.

Therefore, we can find for $v \in V$ an element u in $[A]$ such that for every $z \in [A]$

$$v^{-1}zv = u^{-1}zu. \tag{26}$$

Obviously, v determines the element $u \in [A]$ to within a factor from F. If v ranges over the whole group V, then all the corresponding u of (26) form a subgroup U of $\mathrm{GL}(n/m, K)$ such that $U/F \cong V/F$.

From (26) it follows that

$$v = du, \tag{27}$$

where d belongs to $\mathrm{GL}(n/m, K)$ and is permutable with every element of A. The relations (26) and (27) associate with every coset Fv of V/F the single class Fd. It is easy to see that the product of two classes Fv and Fv_1 is associated with the product of the corresponding classes Fd and Fd_1. If $Fv = Fd \cdot Fu$, $Fv_1 = Fd_1 \cdot Fu_1$, then $FvFv_1 = Fvv_1 = FdFuFd_1Fu_1 = Fdd_1 \cdot Fuu_1$.

Therefore, V/F is homomorphically mapped onto the group D/F, where D is the union of the classes Fd.

Thus, D is a soluble group. We shall now show that $g^{-1}Dg = D$ for every $g \in G$. If $v \in V$, and $v = du$, where $d \in D$, $u \in U$, then $g^{-1}vg = g^{-1}dgg^{-1}ug$, $g^{-1}vg = v_1 \in V$, $g^{-1}ug = u_1 \in g^{-1}[A]g = [A]$.

Hence, it follows that $d_1 = g^{-1}dg$ is permutable with every element of $[A]$. Therefore the element $v_1 = d_1u_1$ determines the same automorphism of the algebra $[A]$ as the element u_1. Consequently, $u_1 \in U$, and d_1 occurs in one of the relations of the form (27), i.e., $d_1 \in D$, $g^{-1}Dg = D$. Now it is easy to prove that $[V] = [A]$. We examine the group GD. GD is soluble. By the maximality of G we have $GD = G$, $D \subset G$. The group D is contained in the centralizer of A in G. By Theorem 4, $D = F$. Therefore, $v = du \in [A]$, $V \subset [A]$, $[V] = [A]$, and the lemma is proved.

2. We shall now investigate the linear P-hull $[G]$ of G.

LEMMA 14. $[G] : P = (G : V)(A : F)(K : P)$.

PROOF. Suppose that $G : V = \nu$ and that $g_1, g_2, \cdots, g_\nu$ is a complete system of coset representatives of V in G. The algebra $[G]$ consists of all expressions of a form

$$v_1g_1 + v_2g_2 + \cdots + v_\nu g_\nu, \tag{28}$$

where the v_i are arbitrary elements of $[V]$.

The elements $g_1, \cdots, g_\nu$ are linearly independent over $[V]$. For suppose that

$$v_1 g_1 + v_2 g_2 + \cdots + v_\nu g_\nu = 0, \qquad v_i \in [V] \tag{29}$$

is a nontrivial relation containing the smallest number of nonzero terms. Let $v_1 \neq 0$, say, when we may assume that also $v_2 \neq 0$.

Since V is the centralizer of F in G and g_1, g_2 lie in distinct cosets of V in G, there is an element f in F such that $f_1 = g_1 f g_1^{-1} \neq f_2 = g_2 f g_2^{-1}$.

From (29) we derive

$$(v_1 g_1 + v_2 g_2 + \cdots + v_\nu g_\nu) f - f_1 (v_1 g_1 + v_2 g_2 + \cdots + v_\nu g_\nu)$$

$$= (f_2 - f_1) v_2 g_2 + \cdots + (f_\nu - f_1) v_\nu g_\nu = 0,$$

where $f_i = g_i f g_i^{-1}$.

The latter relation contradicts the choice of (29). Therefore, $g_1, \cdots, g_\nu$ are linearly independent over $[V]$. Using Lemma 13 we obtain

$$[G] : P = (G : V)([V] : P) = (G : V)([A] : P) = (G : V)(A : F)(K : P).$$

The lemma is now proved.

THEOREM 9. *The order of the factor-group A/F is equal to n^2/m^2, where $m = K : P$.*

PROOF. Lemma 14 gives an expression for the rank of the algebra $[G]$ over P. We now compute the rank of $[G]$ in another way. A comparison of the two expressions for $[G] : P$ will then yield a proof of the lemma.

We have already observed (see Theorem 2) that the index $G : V$ is equal to the number of all the automorphisms of K of the following form

$$x \to g x g^{-1} \qquad x \in K, \quad g \in G. \tag{30}$$

Clearly, all the elements of K that remain fixed under all the automorphisms of the form (30) form a certain field Ω, $K \supseteq \Omega \supseteq P$. Therefore

$$G : V \leqq K : \Omega, \ \frac{1}{\Omega : P} \geqq \frac{G : V}{m}. \tag{31}$$

Let us show that $[G]$ is a simple central algebra over Ω. That $[G]$ is simple follows from the irreducibility of G. We now have to prove that the center of $[G]$ coincides with Ω. Suppose that $z = v_1 g_1 + v_2 g_2 + \cdots + v_\nu g_\nu$, $g_1 = 1$ (see (28)), belongs to the center of $[G]$. Then for every f of F we have $f(v_1 g_1 + v_2 g_2 + \cdots + v_\nu g_\nu) - (v_1 g_1 + v_2 g_2 + \cdots + v_\nu g_\nu) f = 0$. Setting $f_i = g_i f g_i^{-1}$ we obtain $(f-f_1)v_1g_1+(f-f_2)v_2g_2+\cdots+(f-f_\nu)v_\nu g_\nu=0$.

Since $g_1=1$, and $g_2,\cdots,g_\nu$ are linearly independent over $[V]$, we have $(f-f_i)v_i=0$, $i=1,2,\cdots,\nu$. But for every g_i $(i\neq 1)$ we can find in F an element f such that $f_i=g_ifg_i^{-1}\neq f$. Therefore $z=v_1g_1=v_1\in[V]=[A]$.

Since the center of $[A]$ coincides with K, we see that $z\in K$, and from this and (30) it follows that $z\in\Omega$. Thus $[G]$ is a simple central algebra over Ω. If we make use of an Ω-basis of the space $P^{(n)}$, then $P^{(n)}$ can be represented as a t-dimensional space over Ω, where $t=n/(\Omega:P)$. Therefore, we may assume that $[G]$ is contained in the complete matrix algebra Ω_t. We shall show presently that $[G]$ coincides with Ω_t. Suppose that $[G]\subset\Omega_t$. Then by Lemma 6 we can find in $\mathrm{GL}(t,\Omega)\setminus[G]$ a matrix h that commutes with every matrix of $[G]$.

Obviously, the group $(h)G$ is soluble. Also $(h)G\supset G$. The latter inclusion contradicts the maximality of G. Thus $[G]=\Omega_t$. Consequently, $[G]:P=(\Omega_t:\Omega)(\Omega:P)=t^2(\Omega:P)=n^2/(\Omega:P)$. Using (31) we find that $[G]:P\geqq(n^2/m)(G:V)$. By Lemma 14, $[G]:P=(G:V)(A:F)m$. Therefore, $A:F\geqq n^2/m^2$. But earlier it was shown (see (16)) that $A:F\leqq n^2/m^2$. Thus, $A:F=n^2/m^2=r^2$. This proves the theorem.

Theorem 9 can also be written as follows: $[A]=K_r$.

As we have remarked at the beginning of this section, Theorem 9 implies the following

THEOREM 10. *A maximal abelian normal subgroup F of a maximal primitive soluble group G coincides with its centralizer in G if and only if $K:P=n$.*

On the basis of Theorem 9 we can now prove Theorem 4a.

THEOREM 4a. *The centralizer A/F in $\mathrm{GL}(n/m,K)/F$ coincides with A/F.*

For suppose that $c\in\mathrm{GL}(n/m,K)$ and that for every a of A we have $(c,a)\in F$. Then $(c,b_i)=\epsilon_i^{\alpha_i}$, $(a_i,c)=\epsilon_i^{\beta_i}$. If $c_1=a_1^{\alpha_1}b_1^{\beta_1}\cdots a_t^{\alpha_t}b_t^{\beta_t}$, then $(c_1,b_i)=(c,b_i)$, $(a_i,c_1)=(a_i,c)$. Therefore, $(cc_1^{-1},a_i)=(cc_1^{-1},b_i)=1$, $i=1,\cdots,t$. Hence, $(cc_1^{-1},a)=1$ for every $a\in A$. By Theorem 9, $[A]=K_r$, $cc_1^{-1}\in F$, $c=fc_1\in A$.

3. From Theorems 3 and 9 it follows that A contains a system of elements $a_1,b_1,\cdots,a_t,b_t$, such that (i) $(a_i,b_i)=\epsilon_i$, where ϵ_i is a primitive root of the equation $x^{\nu_i}=1$, $\epsilon_i\in K$, (ii) the elements belonging to distinct pairs are permutable, (iii) every element $a\in A$ has a unique representation in the form $a=fa_1^{\alpha_1}b_1^{\beta_1}\cdots a_t^{\alpha_t}b_t^{\beta_t}$, $f\in F$, $0\leqq\alpha_i,\beta_i<\nu_i$,

$$\text{(iv)}\quad \nu_1\nu_2\cdots\nu_t=n/m,\quad \nu_{i+1}/\nu_i. \tag{32}$$

Hence it follows, in particular, that A/F splits into the direct product of $2t$ cyclic subgroups (a_1F), (b_1F), $\cdots$, (a_tF), (b_tF), whose orders are equal to: ν_1, ν_1, $\cdots$, ν_t, ν_t, respectively. Thus A/F is determined to within isomorphism by the decomposition (32) of n/m. Now we shall show that A/F (as an abstract group) is completely determined by n/m. It will turn out that the decomposition (32) must have yet another property: the numbers ν_i are square-free. But it is easy to see that every number r has a unique decomposition of the form $r=\nu_1\nu_2\cdots\nu_t,\ \nu_{i+1}/\nu_i$, where all the ν_i are square-free.

LEMMA 15. *The numbers ν_i in* (32) *are square-free.*

It is sufficient to show that ν_1 is square-free. Let $\nu_i=p^{\alpha_i}s_i$, $(p,s_i)=1$, $i=1,2,\cdots,t$.

Suppose now that $\alpha_1=\alpha_2=\cdots=\alpha_k=\alpha>1$, $\alpha>\alpha_{k+1}$.[4]

We form the elements $c_i=a_i^{s_i}, d_i=b_i^{s_i}$, $i=1,\cdots,t$. The group $A_1=(c_1)(d_1)\cdots(c_t)(d_t)F$ is a normal subgroup of G, because A_1/F is a Sylow p-subgroup of A/F. Next, we form the group $A_2(u_1)(v_1)\cdots(u_k)(v_k)F$, where

$$u_i=c_i^{p^{\alpha-1}},\ v_i=d_i^{p^{\alpha-1}},\qquad i=1,\cdots,k.$$

It is easy to see that A_2 is normal in G. For if $g\in G$, then $gu_ig^{-1}=(gc_ig^{-1})^{p^{\alpha-1}}$, $gc_ig^{-1}\in A_1$, $c_j^{p^{\alpha-1}}d_j^{p^{\alpha-1}}$ belong to F for $j>k$. Therefore, $(gc_ig^{-1})^{p^{\alpha-1}}\in A_2$.

Obviously, $A_2:F=p^{2k}>1$. But A_2 is an abelian group, as is easy to verify. Therefore, $(u_i,v_i)=(a_ib_i)^{s_i^2}p^{2\alpha-2}=\epsilon_i^{s_i^2p^{2\alpha-2}}=1$. Thus A_2 is an abelian normal subgroup of G. This contradicts the maximality of F. Lemma 15 is now proved.

COROLLARY. *A/F is a direct product of cyclic groups of prime orders.*

5. **The factor-group** V/A.

1. Now we shall examine the factor-group V/A.[5] As a preliminary, we mention a few properties of the group A and the algebra $[A]$.

We have already seen (see (32) and above) that the elements

$$a_1^{\alpha_1}b_1^{\beta_1}\cdots a_t^{\alpha_t}b_t^{\beta_t},\qquad 0\leqq\alpha_i,\ \beta_i<\nu_i \tag{33}$$

form, on the one hand, a complete system of coset representatives of F in A, and on the other hand, a K-basis of the algebra $[A]=K_r$.

---

[4] If $k=t$, then we set $\alpha_{k+1}=0$.
[5] See the notation in §4.

LEMMA 16. *Suppose that the elements $c_1, d_1, \cdots, c_t, d_t$ of the algebra $[A]$ are subject to the conditions*: (i) $(c_i, d_i) = (a_i, b_i) = \epsilon_i$, $i = 1, \cdots, t$, (ii) *elements belonging to distinct pairs are permutable,*

$$\text{(iii)} \qquad c_i^{\nu_i} = a_i^{\nu_i}, \quad d_i^{\nu_i} = b_i^{\nu_i}, \qquad i = 1, \cdots, t.$$

Then the mapping $a_i \to c_i$, $b_i \to d_i$, $i = 1, \cdots, t$, can be extended to an automorphism of the algebra $[A] = K_r$.

PROOF. The system of all the elements of the form

$$c_1^{\alpha_1} d_1^{\beta_1} \cdots c_t^{\alpha_t} d_t^{\beta_t}, \qquad 0 \leqq \alpha_i,\ \beta_i < \nu_i, \tag{34}$$

is linearly independent over K.

For if $u = c_1^{\alpha_1} d_1^{\beta_1} \cdots d_t^{\beta_t}$ and $v = c_1^{\gamma_1} d_1^{\delta_1} \cdots d_t^{\delta_t}$ are elements of (34) and $\alpha_1 \neq \gamma_1$, then $(d_1, u) \neq (d_1, v)$, $(u, v) \in F$.

Therefore, we can apply the arguments in the proof of Lemma 10 and can claim the linear independence of the system (34). Since the number of elements of (34) is equal to r^2, this system is a basis of $[A]$.

If

$$(a_1^{\alpha_1} b_1^{\beta_1} \cdots b_t^{\beta_t})(a_1^{\gamma_1} b_1^{\delta_1} \cdots b_t^{\delta_t}) = f a_1^{\lambda_1} b_1^{\mu_1} \cdots b_t^{\mu_t}$$

$$f \in F, \quad \lambda_i \equiv \alpha_i + \gamma_i, \quad \mu_i \equiv \beta_i + \delta_i \pmod{\nu_i},$$

then we obtain from the conditions (i), (ii) and (iii) of Lemma 16

$$(c_1^{\alpha_1} d_1^{\beta_1} \cdots d_t^{\beta_t})(c_1^{\gamma_1} d_1^{\delta_1} \cdots d_t^{\delta_t}) = f c_1^{\lambda_1} d_1^{\mu_1} \cdots d_t^{\mu_t}.$$

In other words, the structure constants of $[A]$ do not change on transition from the basis (33) to (34).

Therefore, there exists an automorphism σ of the algebra $[A]$ such that $a_i^\sigma = c_i$, $b_i^\sigma = d_i$, $i = 1, \cdots, t$.

Since every automorphism of $[A] = K_r$ is inner, $\mathrm{GL}(r, K)$ contains a matrix S such that $S^{-1} a_i S = c_i$, $S^{-1} b_i S = d_i$, $i = 1, \cdots, t$.

2. Now let $n/m = q_1^{l_1} q_2^{l_2} \cdots q_k^{l_k}$ be the canonical decomposition of $r = n/m$. Then by Lemma 15 (see the corollary), the factor-group A/F can be represented as the direct product of $2(l_1 + \cdots + l_k)$ cyclic groups of prime orders: $2l_i$ factors of order q_i, $i = 1, 2, \cdots, k$.

The cyclic factors of order q_i can be chosen in the form $(a_j^{\tau_{ij}} F)$, $(b_j^{\tau_{ij}} F)$, where $\tau_{ij} = \nu_j / q_i$. It is easy to verify that $(a_j^{\tau_{ij}}, b_j^{\tau_{ij}})$ is a primitive root of the equation $x^{q_i} = 1$. Further, if $(i - \lambda)^2 + (j - \mu)^2 \neq 0$, then $(a_j^{\tau_{ij}}, a_\mu^{\tau_{\lambda\mu}}) = (a_j^{\tau_{ij}}, b_\mu^{\tau_{\lambda\mu}}) = (b_j^{\tau_{ij}}, b_\mu^{\tau_{\lambda\mu}}) = 1$.

Hence, it follows that the group A can be represented in the form $A = (a_{11})(b_{11}) \cdots (a_{1l_1})(b_{1l_1}) \cdots (a_{k1})(b_{k1}) \cdots (a_{kl_k})(b_{kl_k}) F$, where

$$(a_{ij}, b_{ij}) = \eta_i, \ \eta_i^{q_i} = 1, \ \eta_i \neq 1, (a_{ij}, a_{\mu\lambda}) = (a_{ij}, b_{\mu\lambda})$$
$$= (b_{ij}, b_{\mu\lambda}) = 1 \text{ for } (i-\lambda)^2 + (j-\mu)^2 \neq 0, \ a_{ij}^{q_i}, \ b_{ij}^{q_i} \in F. \tag{35}$$

Obviously, all the elements of the form

$$a_{11}^{\alpha_{11}} b_{11}^{\beta_{11}} \cdots b_{1l_1}^{\beta_{1l_1}} \cdots b_{kl_k}^{\beta_{kl_k}}, \qquad 0 \leq \alpha_{ij}, \beta_{ij} < q_i \tag{36}$$

constitute a complete system of coset representatives of F in A.

It is also clear that Lemma 16 remains valid for systems of the form $a_{11}, b_{11}; \cdots; a_{1l_1}, b_{1l_1}; \cdots; a_{k1}, b_{k1}; \cdots; a_{kl_k}, b_{kl_k}$, (i) satisfying the conditions (35).

We note one other proposition.

Every system formed from several pairs of (i) generates a simple algebra over K.

For suppose, for example, that the system consists of a single pair: a, b,[6] $(a, b) = \eta$, η a primitive root of the equation $x^q = 1$, $\eta \in F$, a^q, $b^q \in F$. We have to show that the linear K-hull $[B]$ of the group $B = (a)(b)F$ is a simple algebra.

The elements of $[B]$ have the form $\sum \lambda_{\alpha\beta} a^\alpha b^\beta$, $\lambda_{\alpha\beta} \in K$, $0 \leq \alpha$, $\beta < q$. Now let $N_0 \neq 0$ be a two-sided ideal of $[B]$ and c an element of N_0 containing not fewer than two nonzero terms:

$$c = \lambda a^\alpha b^\beta + \mu a^{\alpha_1} b^{\beta_1} + \cdots$$
$$(\alpha - \alpha_1)^2 + (\beta - \beta_1)^2 \neq 0.$$

Suppose that $\beta \neq \beta_1$, say,

$$c_1 = \eta^\beta c - aca^{-1} = \mu(\eta^\beta - \eta^{\beta_1}) a^{\alpha_1} b^{\beta_1} + \cdots,$$

$c_1 \neq 0$ contains fewer terms than c and belongs to N_0.

Hence, it follows that N_0 contains elements of the form $\rho a^\gamma b^\delta \in B$. Therefore, $B \subset N_0$, $[B] = N_0$. This proves that $[B]$ is simple.

3. We now proceed to investigate V/A.

Every element v of V determines an automorphism σ_v of A:

$$x \to \sigma_v(x) = vxv^{-1}, \qquad x \in A. \tag{37}$$

Since $\sigma_v(F) = F$, σ_v induces an automorphism $\bar{\sigma}_v$ of the factor-group A/F:

$$\bar{\sigma}_v(xF) = \sigma_v(x)F.$$

It is easy to verify that the correspondence

$$v \to \bar{\sigma}_v \tag{39}$$

is a homomorphism. By Theorem 4, the kernel of (39) coincides with A.

[6] Indices are omitted.

Therefore, the factor-group V/A is isomorphic to the group of all automorphisms of the form $\bar{\sigma}_v$ of A/F. If now $A/F=Q_1/F\,Q_2/F\cdots Q_k/F$ is the decomposition of A/F into the direct product of primary factors, then $\bar{\sigma}_v(Q_i/F)=Q_i/F$.

Obviously, $Q_1=(a_{11})(b_{11})\cdots(a_{1l_1})(b_{1l_1})F$, etc. Therefore,

$$\left.\begin{aligned}\sigma_v(a_{1i})&=f_i\,a_{11}^{\alpha_{1i}}b_{11}^{\gamma_{1i}}\cdots a_{1l_1}^{\alpha_{l_1 i}}b_{1l_1}^{\gamma_{l_1 i}}=a_{1i}^{1}\\ \sigma_v(b_{1i})&=\phi_i a_{11}^{\beta_{1i}}b_{11}^{\delta_{1i}}\cdots a_{1l_1}^{\beta_{l_1 i}}b_{1l_1}^{\delta_{l_1 i}}=b_{1i}^{1}\end{aligned}\right\} \tag{40}$$

$$i=1,\cdots,l_1,\ f_i,\ \phi_i\in F,\quad 0\leqq\alpha_{\rho i},\ \beta_{\rho i},\ \gamma_{\rho i},\ \delta_{\rho i}<q_1$$

$$\rho=1,\cdots,l_1.$$

Similar expressions hold for $\sigma_v(a_{ji})$, $\sigma_v(b_{ji})$, $j=2,\cdots,k$.

Obviously,

$$\begin{aligned}(a_{1i}',b_{1i}')&=\eta_1, & (a_{1i}',a_{1\mu}')&=1,\\ (a_{1i}',b_{1\mu}')&=1, & (b_{1i}',b_{1\mu}')&=1,\end{aligned} \tag{41}$$

where $i\neq\mu$, $\eta_1^{q_1}=1$, $\eta_1\neq 1$.

Hence, it is easy to derive the following four systems of equations

$$\left.\begin{aligned}&\sum_{\rho=1}^{l_1}(\alpha_{\rho i}\delta_{\rho i}-\beta_{\rho i}\gamma_{\rho i})\equiv 1\\ &\qquad i=1,\cdots,l_1\\ &\sum_{\rho=1}^{l_1}(\alpha_{\rho i}\gamma_{\rho\mu}-\alpha_{\rho\mu}\gamma_{\rho i})\equiv 0\\ &\qquad \mu\neq i\\ &\sum_{\rho=1}^{l_1}(\alpha_{\rho i}\delta_{\rho\mu}-\beta_{\rho i}\gamma_{\rho\mu})\equiv 0\\ &\qquad \mu\neq i\\ &\sum_{\rho=1}^{l_1}(\beta_{\rho i}\delta_{\rho\mu}-\beta_{\rho\mu}\delta_{\rho i})\equiv 0\\ &\qquad \mu\neq i\end{aligned}\right\}(\mathrm{mod}\,q_1). \tag{42}$$

Let us now examine, for example, the relations

$$(a_{1i}',b_{1i}')=\eta_1,\quad \eta_1=(a_{11}^{\alpha_{1i}}b_{11}^{\gamma_{1i}}\cdots b_{1l_1}^{\gamma_{l_1 i}},\quad a_{11}^{\delta_{1i}}\cdots b_{1l_1}^{\delta_{l_1 i}})$$
$$=(a_{11}^{\alpha_{1i}},b_{11}^{\delta_{1i}})(b_{11}^{\gamma_{1i}},a_{11}^{\beta_{1i}})\cdots(a_{1l_1}^{\alpha_{l_1 i}},b_{1l_1}^{\delta_{l_1 i}})(b_{1l_1}^{\gamma_{l_1 i}},a_{1l_1}^{\beta_{l_1 i}})$$
$$=\eta_1^{\Delta_{1i}+\cdots+\Delta_{l_1 i}},\ \text{where } \Delta_{\rho j}=\alpha_{\rho j}\delta_{\rho j}-\beta_{\rho j}\gamma_{\rho j}.$$

Hence $\sum_{\rho=1}^{l_1}\Delta_{\rho j}\equiv 1(\operatorname{mod} q_1)$, and this is equivalent to the first system of equations (42). The same computations also lead to the remaining three systems (42). Obviously, the formulae (40) can be rewritten in the form

$$\left.\begin{aligned}\bar{\sigma}_v(a_{1i}F) &= a_{11}^{\alpha_{1i}}b_{11}^{\gamma_{1i}}\cdots b_{1l_1}^{\gamma_{l_1 i}}F\\ \bar{\sigma}_v(b_{1i}F) &= a_{11}^{\beta_{1i}}b_{11}^{\delta_{1i}}\cdots b_{1l_1}^{\delta_{l_1 i}}F\end{aligned}\right\} \qquad (40')$$

$$i=1,2,\cdots,l_1,$$

where $\alpha_{\rho j}, \beta_{\rho j}, \gamma_{\rho j}, \delta_{\rho j}$ can be regarded as elements of the finite field $\mathrm{GF}(q_1)$.

Therefore, the automorphism $\bar{\sigma}_v$ is given by k matrices of the form

$$S=\begin{bmatrix}\alpha_{11} & \beta_{11} & \cdots & \alpha_{1l} & \beta_{1l}\\ \gamma_{11} & \delta_{11} & \cdots & \gamma_{1l} & \delta_{1l}\\ \cdot & \cdot & \cdots & \cdot & \cdot\\ \cdot & \cdot & \cdots & \cdot & \cdot\\ \alpha_{l1} & \beta_{l1} & \cdots & \alpha_{ll} & \beta_{ll}\\ \gamma_{l1} & \delta_{l1} & \cdots & \gamma_{ll} & \delta_{ll}\end{bmatrix}$$

where $\alpha_{\rho j}, \beta_{\rho j}, \gamma_{\rho j}, \delta_{\rho j}$ belong to $\mathrm{GL}(q)$ and are subject to the conditions (42).

It is not difficult to verify that the equation (42), considered as an equation in $\mathrm{GF}(q)$, is equivalent to

$$S\Phi S'=\Phi \qquad \text{where} \qquad \Phi=E_l\times\begin{bmatrix}0 & 1\\ -1 & 0\end{bmatrix}. \qquad (42')$$

The set of all matrices S subject to (42′) is, of course, the symplectic group $S_p(2l,q)$. So we have

THEOREM 11. *Let $n/m=q_1^{l_1}q_2^{l_2}\cdots q_k^{l_k}$ be the canonical decomposition of n/m. Then the factor-group V/A is isomorphic to a soluble subgroup of the direct product of the k symplectic groups $S_p(2l_1,q_1),\cdots,S_p(2l_k,q_k)$.*

For the following, it is important to note that for $l=1$ the symplectic group $S_p(2l,q)$ coincides with the special linear group $\mathrm{SL}(2,q)$.

4. We have seen that a maximal primitive soluble subgroup G of $\mathrm{GL}(n,P)$ is an extension of the group $A=(a_1)(b_1)\cdots(b_l)F$ (see §5).

Now let us find out under what conditions an extension Γ of A contained in $\mathrm{GL}(n,P)$ is a primitive group. We shall restrict ourselves here to the case when F coincides with the multiplicative group of the field PE_n.

Suppose that Γ is contained in $\mathrm{GL}(n,P)$ and contains $A=(a_1)(b_1)\cdots(b_t)F$ as a normal subgroup. Let $n=q_1^{l_1}q_2^{l_2}\cdots q_k^{k}$ be the canonical decomposition of n.

By Theorem 4a, the centralizer of A/F in Γ/F coincides with A/F. Therefore, the arguments under 3. above are applicable to Γ/A, i.e., Γ/A is isomorphic to a certain subgroup of the direct product of the k symplectic groups

$$S_p(2l_1, q_1) \cdots S_p(2l_k, q_k).$$

Suppose now that Γ is primitive and that

$$P^{(n)} = R_1 + R_2 + \cdots + R_\tau, \qquad \tau > 1$$

is the decomposition of $P^{(n)}$ into systems of primitivity of Γ. Every element g of Γ produces a certain permutation S_g of degree τ on the subspaces $R_1, \cdots, R_\tau$. The homomorphism $g \rightarrow S_g$ determines a homomorphism $a \rightarrow S_a$, where $a \in A$.

If Γ_0 is the kernel of the first homomorphism, then $A_0 = A \cap \Gamma_0$ is the kernel of the second. Since $A_0 \supseteq F$, then A/A_0 is an abelian group. Since A is irreducible, A/A_0 is isomorphic to a transitive subgroup of the symmetric group S_τ. Therefore, $A : A_0 = \tau$. Since $A_0 = A \cap \Gamma_0$, then, A_0 is a normal subgroup of Γ. Since every system of distinct coset representatives of F in A is linearly independent, $A_0 : F = [A_0] : P = n^2/\tau$.

By Clifford's theorem $[A_0]$ is a completely reducible algebra and all the blocks $[A_\nu]$ have one and the same degree $\rho \leqq n/\tau$. Therefore, $A_0 : F = [A] : P \leqq \rho^2 n/\rho = \rho n \leqq n^2/\tau$.

Hence it follows that $\rho = n/\tau$ and that $[A_0]$ splits into τ irreducible inequivalent blocks and is not a simple algebra. We decompose A/F and A_0/F into direct factors

$$A/F = Q_1/F\, Q_2/F \cdots Q_k/F,$$

$$A_0/F = Q_1'/F\, Q_2'/F \cdots Q_\nu'/F, \qquad \nu \leqq k,$$

$$Q_i : F = q_i^{2l_i}, \quad Q_1' \subseteq Q_1, \cdots, Q_\nu' \subseteq Q_\nu.$$

For at least one i

$$Q_i' \neq Q_i.$$

For if we have $Q_i' = Q_i$ for all $i = 1, \cdots, \nu$, then $A_0 = Q_1 Q_2 \cdots Q_\nu$ and, consequently, by the proposition at the end of 2. $[A_0]$ is a simple algebra.

Obviously Q_i' is a normal subgroup of Γ. Since $Q_i' \neq Q_i$, the soluble subgroup of $S_p(2l_i, q_i)$ determined by Γ is reducible.

Therefore, *if all the subgroups of the symplectic groups* $S_p(2l_1, q_1) \cdots S_p(2l_k, q_k)$ *induced by* Γ *are irreducible, then* Γ *is primitive.*

5. $GL(n, P)$ does not always have soluble primitive subgroups.

THEOREM 12. *If there are soluble primitive subgroups in* $\mathrm{GL}(n, P)$, *then the field* P *has an extension* K *such that the degree* $K:P=m$ *divides* n *and that for every prime divisor* q *of* n/m *a primitive root of the equation* $x^q=1$ *is contained in* K.

PROOF. Suppose that $\mathrm{GL}(n, P)$ has primitive soluble subgroups. Then we can find at least one maximal primitive soluble subgroup G in $\mathrm{GL}(n, P)$. The maximal abelian normal subgroup F of this group is the multiplicative group of a certain field K, $K \subset P_n$, $K:P=m$, m/n. If $m=n$, then the theorem is proved. But if $m<n$, then G has a normal series: $G \supseteq V \supseteq A \supset F \supset E$, $A:F=n^2/m^2$, $A=(a_1)(b_1)\cdots(a_t)(b_t)F$, $(a_i, b_i)=\epsilon_i \in K$, ϵ_i is a primitive root of the equation $x^{\nu_i}=1$,

$$\nu_1\nu_2\cdots\nu_t=n/m.$$

Therefore, K contains, for every prime divisor q of n/m, a primitive root of the equation $x^q=1$. This proves the theorem.

In particular, *if the field* P *is algebraically closed, then for the existence of primitive soluble subgroups in* $\mathrm{GL}(n, P)$ *it is necessary that the characteristic of* P *should either be zero or be prime to* n.

In the second chapter we shall prove that the latter condition is also sufficient for the existence of primitive soluble subgroups of $\mathrm{GL}(n, P)$, provided P is algebraically closed. For an odd n we have the following criterion: if n is an odd number, then $\mathrm{GL}(n, P)$ has primitive soluble subgroups if and only if P has an extension K such that $K:P=m$ divides n and that for every prime factor q of n/m K contains a primitive root of the equation $x^q=1$.

6. **Imprimitive soluble subgroups of** $\mathrm{GL}(n, P)$.

1. Suppose that the maximal soluble irreducible subgroup Γ of $\mathrm{GL}(n, P)$ is imprimitive. We shall try to find the structure of a maximal abelian normal subgroup of Γ.

THEOREM 13. *A maximal abelian normal subgroup* Φ *of* Γ *is the direct product of* ν *copies of the multiplicative group of a certain field* $K \subseteq P_{n/\nu}$ *whose degree* $K:P$ *divides the number* n/ν.

PROOF. By Clifford's theorem, the space $P^{(n)}$ can be represented in the form of a direct sum of νl subspaces Q_{ij}, invariant and irreducible relative to Φ, $i=1,\cdots,\nu$, $j=1,\cdots,l$; also Φ induces equivalent representations in the Q_{ij} with equal first indices, and the ν direct sums

$$D_i = Q_{i1} + \cdots + Q_{il} \qquad i = 1, 2, \cdots, \nu \tag{43}$$

are systems of imprimitivity of Γ.

We now examine the linear P-hull $[\Phi]$ of Φ. The set of all linear transformations induced by $[\Phi]$ in D_i forms a field K_i, $K_i : P = Q_{ij} : P = n/(\nu l)$. Let $g_i \in \Gamma$ and $g_i(D_1) = D_i$. Then $[\Phi] = g_i[\Phi]g_i^{-1}$. Hence, it follows that the ν fields $K_1, \cdots, K_\nu$ are isomorphic.

Now let $\bar{\Phi}_i$ be the multiplicative group of K_i. In GL(n, P) we construct the subgroup $\Phi_i \simeq \bar{\Phi}_i$ whose elements leave all the vectors of D_j fixed, $j \neq i$, and act in D_i like the elements of $\bar{\Phi}_i$. The theorem will be proved if we can show that $\Phi = \Phi_1 \Phi_2 \cdots \Phi_\nu$.

Obviously, $\Phi_1 \Phi_2 \cdots \Phi_\nu \supseteq \Phi$. On the other hand, if $g \in \Gamma$ and $g(D_i) = D_j$, then $g\Phi_i g^{-1} = \Phi_j$. Therefore, $g\Phi_1 \Phi_2 \cdots \Phi_\nu g^{-1} = \Phi_1 \Phi_2 \cdots \Phi_\nu$, $\Gamma\Phi_1 \cdots \Phi_\nu = \Phi_1 \cdots \Phi_\nu \Gamma$ is a soluble group. Since Γ is maximal, we have $\Phi_1 \Phi_2 \cdots \Phi_\nu \subset \Gamma$. Also, since Φ is maximal, we have $\Phi_1 \Phi_2 \cdots \Phi_\nu = \Phi$.

This completes the proof.

THEOREM 14. *A maximal irreducible soluble subgroup of the full linear group over an infinite field has a unique maximal abelian normal subgroup.*

PROOF. We shall show, first of all, that the index of a maximal abelian normal subgroup Φ of a maximal soluble irreducible group Γ is finite.

We consider the subgroup H_i consisting of all elements of Γ that permute the vectors of D_i inside D_i (see (43)). The subgroups $H_1, \cdots, H_\nu$ are conjugate in Γ and H_i induces in D_i an irreducible subgroup Γ^i of GL$(n/\nu, P)$ (see Lemma 1 and above). Now we shall show that $\bar{\Phi}_i$ is a maximal abelian normal subgroup of Γ^i. Suppose that Γ^1 has an abelian normal subgroup $\bar{\Psi}^1 \supset \bar{\Phi}_1$. We construct the group $\Psi^1 \subset$ GL(n, P) whose elements act in D_i like those of $\bar{\Psi}^1$ and leave the vectors of the subspaces $D_2, \cdots, D_\nu$ fixed. Now, if $g_1 = 1$, $g_2, \cdots, g_\nu \in \Gamma$ and $g_i(D_1) = D_i$, then 1, $g_2, \cdots, g_\nu$ is a complete system of left coset representatives of H_1 in Γ (see § 1). We set $\Psi^i = g_1 \Psi^1 g_i^{-1}$. Obviously, $\Psi^i \supset \Phi_i$. Furthermore, $g\Psi^1 \cdots \Psi^\nu g^{-1} = g\Psi^1 g^{-1} \cdots g\Psi^\nu g^{-1} = \Psi^1 \cdots \Psi^\nu$.

Therefore $\Psi^1 \Psi^2 \cdots \Psi^\nu \Gamma = \Gamma \Psi^1 \cdots \Psi^\nu$ is a soluble group. Since Γ is maximal, $\Psi = \Psi^1 \cdots \Psi^\nu \subset \Gamma$. Ψ is an abelian normal subgroup of Γ, $\Psi \supset \Phi$, but this is impossible. So $\bar{\Phi}_i$ is a maximal abelian normal subgroup of Γ^i.

By Theorem 5, $\Gamma^i : \Phi_i \leq \rho(n/\nu)$. Therefore,

$$\Gamma : \Phi \leq \nu! \, (\rho(n/\nu))^\nu. \tag{44}$$

We now proceed to the proof of Theorem 14. Let

$$P^{(n)} = Q_1 + Q_2 + \cdots + Q_k \tag{45}$$

be the complete decomposition of $P^{(n)}$ into systems of imprimitivity of Γ. By Lemma 5, $\Gamma = TG$, where T is isomorphic to a maximal soluble transitive subgroup of the symmetric group S_k, and $G = G_1 G_2 \cdots G_k$, where G_i acts on Q_i like a maximal primitive soluble subgroup of $\mathrm{GL}(n/k, P)$ and the vectors of Q_j, $j \neq i$, remain fixed. By Theorem 7, G_i has a unique maximal abelian normal subgroup F_i.

We set $F = F_1 F_2 \cdots F_k$. Obviously F is an abelian normal subgroup of Γ and

$$\Gamma : F \leqq k! \, (\rho(n/k))^k. \tag{46}$$

The theorem will be proved if we can establish that the maximal abelian normal subgroup Φ of Γ coincides with F. We examine the intersection $\Phi \cap F_j$, $j = 1, \cdots, k$. $\Phi \cap F_j$ is not trivial, because on the one hand, $F_j : (\Phi \cap F_j) = \Phi F_j : \Phi \leqq \Gamma : \Phi \leqq \nu! \, (\rho(n/\nu))^\nu$. On the other hand, F_j is an infinite group. Therefore $\Phi \cap F$ contains k matrices of the form

$$t_j = \begin{bmatrix} E_{n/k} & & & & & & \\ & \cdot & & & & & \\ & & \cdot & & & & \\ & & & N_j & & & \\ & & & & \cdot & & \\ & & & & & \cdot & \\ & & & & & & E_{n/k} \end{bmatrix}, \qquad j = 1, \cdots, k,$$

where the jth diagonal block N_j is different from the unit matrices of order n/k.[7] F_j acts in Q_j like the multiplicative group of a certain field K_j. Therefore, $N_j \subseteq K_j \subseteq P_{n/k}$. Now let

$$\phi = \begin{bmatrix} \phi_{11} & \phi_{12} & \cdots & \phi_{1k} \\ \phi_{21} & \phi_{22} & \cdots & \phi_{2k} \\ \cdot & \cdot & \cdots & \cdot \\ \cdot & \cdot & \cdots & \cdot \\ \phi_{k1} & \phi_{k2} & \cdots & \phi_{kk} \end{bmatrix},$$

where the matrix ϕ_{ij} of order n/k over P belongs to Φ. Then

$$\phi t_j = t_j \phi.$$

Hence, we have for $i \neq j$,

[7] Here we have in mind the basis of $P^{(n)}$ that was adapted in the decomposition (45).

$$\phi_{ij}(N_j - E_{n/k}) = 0.$$

Since $N_j - E_{n/k}$ belongs to the field K_j and $N_j \neq E_{n/k}$, we have $\phi_{ij} = 0$ when $i \neq j$, i.e.,

$$\phi = \begin{bmatrix} \phi_{11} & & & \\ & \phi_{22} & & \\ & & \ddots & \\ & & & \phi_{kk} \end{bmatrix}, \qquad \phi \in G = G_1 \cdots G_k.$$

Therefore

$$d_j = \begin{bmatrix} E_{n/k} & & & & \\ & \ddots & & & \\ & & \phi_{jj} & & \\ & & & \ddots & \\ & & & & E_{n/k} \end{bmatrix} \in G_j.$$

Since F_j is the unique maximal abelian normal subgroup of G_j, we have $d_j \in F_j$, $\phi \in F_1 F_2 \cdots F_k = F$, $\Phi \subseteq F$. Since Φ is maximal, $\Phi = F$. This proves the theorem.

THEOREM 15.[8] *Every irreducible soluble subgroup of* GL(n, P) *has an abelian normal subgroup whose index does not exceed the number*

$$n!\,(\rho(n))^n = \tau(n).$$

PROOF. Let Γ_1 be an irreducible soluble subgroup of GL(n, P) and $P^{(n)} = Q_1 + Q_2 + \cdots + Q_k$ the complete decomposition of $P^{(n)}$ into systems of imprimitivity of Γ_1. Γ_1 is contained in the group $\Gamma' = T'G'$, with T' isomorphic to a certain subgroup of the symmetric group S_k and the normal subgroup G' consisting of all the matrices of the form

$$\begin{bmatrix} b_1 & & & \\ & b_2 & & \\ & & \ddots & \\ & & & b_k \end{bmatrix}$$

where the b_i independently range over a certain maximal soluble primitive subgroup of GL$(n/k, P)$ (see (8a)). Obviously, Γ has an abelian normal subgroup F whose index is less than $k!\,(\rho(n/k))^k < n!(\rho(n))^n$, $\Gamma_1 \cap F$ is an abelian normal subgroup of Γ_1, $\Gamma_1 : (\Gamma_1 \cap F) = \Gamma_1 F : F \leqq \Gamma' : F < n!\,(\rho(n))^n$. The theorem is now proved.

[8] See the proof of Theorem 1 in the paper by A. I. Mal′cev [**12**] and of Theorem 3 in our paper [**15**]

3. THE THEOREM OF ZASSENHAUS [28].

THEOREM 16. *The length of the derived series of a soluble subgroup of* GL(n, P) *does not exceed a certain number* $\lambda(n)$ *depending only on* n.

PROOF. Let Γ be a soluble subgroup of GL(n, P). If Γ is irreducible, then it follows from Theorem 15 that the derived length of Γ does not exceed the number $\log_2 \tau(n)+1$. But if Γ is reducible and contains k irreducible parts, then by (3) the derived length does not exceed the number

$$\log_2 \tau(n)+n=\lambda(n).$$

This proves the theorem.

THEOREM 17. *Every locally soluble subgroup of a full linear group is soluble.*

PROOF. We introduce the commutators D^j

$$D^1(g_1,g_2)=g_1g_2g_1^{-1}g_2^{-1},$$
$$D^j=D^1(D^{j-1}(g_1,\cdots,g_{2^{j-1}}),\ D^{j-1}(g_{2^{j-1}+1},\cdots,g_{2^j})).$$

Now a group in which $D^k=1$ for all elements, is soluble with a derived length not exceeding k. Let G_0 be a locally soluble subgroup of GL(n, P). Then for all elements of G_0 we have $D^k=1$ with $k=\lambda(n)$ (see Theorem 16). Therefore, G_0 is soluble.

A maximal soluble normal subgroup of a group is called a radical.

Since the product of two soluble normal subgroups is again a soluble normal subgroup, a group can only have one radical.

THEOREM 18. *Every subgroup of the full linear group has a radical.*

PROOF. Let G_0 be a subgroup of GL(n, P). The set of all soluble normal subgroups of G_0 generates a normal subgroup N of G_0 (Kuroš [7, p. 66]). Every finite set of elements of N is contained in the product of a finite number of soluble normal subgroups of G_0, consequently, in a certain soluble normal subgroup.

Thus, N is a locally soluble normal subgroup of G_0. By Theorem 17, N is a soluble normal subgroup of G_0. Hence, the theorem follows.

CHAPTER II

SOLUBLE LINEAR GROUPS OVER A FINITE FIELD. SOLUBLE LINEAR GROUPS OVER AN ALGEBRAICALLY CLOSED FIELD

1. On soluble groups of permutations. The attempt to construct all soluble primitive subgroups of the symmetric group led to the investigation of soluble subgroups of the full linear group over a finite field (E. Galois, C. Jordan).

Suppose that G_0 is a primitive soluble subgroup of the symmetric group S_N of degree N. Then G_0 has a nontrivial abelian normal subgroup A_0. Since a normal subgroup of a primitive group is a transitive, A_0 is an abelian transitive subgroup of order N. The group A_0 does not have characteristic subgroups, i.e., A_0 is a direct product of cyclic groups of one and the same prime order p. Consequently, $N=p^n$. Obviously, G_0 is a subgroup of the normalizer K_0 of A_0 in S_{p^n}. We shall now construct K_0. Let $u_1, \cdots, u_n$ be a basis of A_0. We label the symbols to be permuted by S_{p^n} by means of n-dimensional vectors $(\alpha_1, \alpha_2, \cdots, \alpha_n)$ over $\mathrm{GF}(p)$. Let $(0,0,\cdots,0)$ be one of the symbols to be permuted; then $(\alpha_1,\alpha_2,\cdots,\alpha_n)$ shall denote that symbol into which the permutation $a=u_1^{\alpha_1}u_2^{\alpha_2}\cdots u_n^{\alpha_n}$ carries $(0,0,\cdots,0)$. If $k\in K_0$, then $k(0,0,\cdots,0)=(\beta_1,\beta_2,\cdots,\beta_n)$, $\beta_i\in\mathrm{GF}(p)$. Obviously,

$$ku_jk^{-1}=u_1^{\alpha_{1j}}u_2^{\alpha_{2j}}\cdots u_n^{\alpha_{nj}}, \qquad ku_j^{x_j}k^{-1}=u_1^{\alpha_{1j}x_j}u_2^{\alpha_{2j}x_j}\cdots u_n^{\alpha_{nj}x_j},$$

$$j=1,2,\cdots,n.$$

Hence,

$$ku_1^{x_1}u_2^{x_2}\cdots u_n^{x_n}k^{-1}=u_1^{\sigma_1}u_2^{\sigma_2}\cdots u_n^{\sigma_n}$$

where $\sigma_i=\sum_{j=1}^n\alpha_{ij}x_j$.

Further,

$$ku_1^{x_1}u_2^{x_2}\cdots u_n^{x_n}=u_1^{\sigma_1}u_2^{\sigma_2}\cdots u_n^{\sigma_n}k.$$

Applying both sides of the last equation to the symbol $(0,0,\cdots,0)$ we obtain

$$k(x_1,x_2,\cdots,x_n)=\left(\sum_{j=1}^n\alpha_{1j}x_j+\beta_1,\cdots,\sum_{j=1}^n\alpha_{nj}x_j+\beta_n\right).$$

Therefore, $K_0=\mathrm{GL}(n,P)A_0$.

Since $K_0\supseteq G_0\supset A_0$, we have $G_0=\Gamma A_0$ where Γ is a soluble subgroup of $\mathrm{GL}(n,P)$. It is not difficult to show that the primitivity of the subgroup G_0 of the symmetric group S_{pn} implies the irreducibility of the subgroup Γ of the full linear group $\mathrm{GL}(n,P)$, and conversely, if Γ_1 is a soluble irreducible subgroup of $\mathrm{GL}(n,P)$, then $G_{01}=\Gamma_1A_0$ is a primitive soluble subgroup of S_{pn}. From this there follows *Jordan's Theorem*: the number of nonconjugate maximal primitive soluble subgroups of the symmetric group S_{pn} is equal to the number of nonconjugate maximal subgroups of $\mathrm{GL}(n,P)$.

2. **Primitive soluble subgroups of the full linear group over a finite field.** Let Γ be a maximal primitive soluble subgroup of $\mathrm{GL}(n,P^l)$. By Theorem 1, an abelian normal subgroup F of Γ is the multiplicative group of a field $K=\mathrm{GF}(p^{ml})$, m/n.

Therefore, F is a cyclic group of order $p^{ml}-1$.

Here, two cases are possible: (a) $m=n$, (b) $m<n$. Let $m=n$. Then $K=\mathrm{GF}(p^{ml})$. The space[9] $P^{(n)}$ in which Γ acts can be represented in the form $P^{(n)}=Ku_0$, where u_0 is an arbitrary nonzero vector of $P^{(n)}$ Suppose that $g\in\Gamma$ and that f is an element of order $P^{nl}-1$ of F.

The matrices f and $f_1=gfg^{-1}$ are roots of one and the same irreducible polynomial of $P[x]$. Therefore, $f_1=f^{\tau}$, $\tau=p^{lj}$, $0\leqq j<n$. Since $P^{(n)}=Ku_0$, the equation

$$g_0(\lambda u_0)=\lambda^{p^l}u_0,$$

where λ ranges over the whole field K, uniquely determines an element g_0 of $\mathrm{GL}(n,P^l)$. It is easy to verify the following relations:

$$g_0fg_0^{-1}(\lambda u_0)=f^{p^l}\lambda u_0, \qquad g_0fg_0^{-1}=f^{p^l},$$

$$g_0^jfg_0^{-j}=f^{\tau}=f_1=gfg^{-1}, \qquad \tau=p^{lj}.$$

Since F coincides with its centralizer in $\mathrm{GL}(n,P)$ for $m=n$, we have $g_0^{-j}g\in F$.

Therefore, $g_0F, g_0^2F,\cdots,g_0^{n-1}F$ are the cosets of F in Γ. Then Γ is completely determined. The order of Γ is $n(p^{nl}-1)$ and Γ/F is a cyclic group. The elements g of Γ are given by the equation

$$g(\lambda u_0)=u\lambda^{p^{lj}}u_0, \qquad u\in F. \tag{1}$$

The group of operators (1) was first constructed by E. Galois.

[9] $P=\mathrm{GF}(p^l)$.

Now let $m<n$. Then by Theorem 10 the centralizer of F in Γ is different from F and Γ has the series

$$\Gamma \supseteq V \supseteq A \supset F \supset E. \tag{2}$$

By Theorem 2 the factor-group Γ/F is a cyclic group whose order divides m and A/F is an abelian normal subgroup of Γ/F, $A:F=n^2/m^2$. As was shown above, the elements a of A admit the representation

$$a=fa_1^{\alpha_1}b_1^{\beta_1}\cdots a_t^{\alpha_t}b_t^{\beta_t}, \tag{3}$$

$f\in F$, $(a_i, b_i)=\epsilon_i\in F$, ϵ_i a primitive root of $x^{\nu_i}=1$;

$$(a_i, a_j)=(a_i, b_j)=(b_i, b_j)=1 \text{ for } i\neq j;\ 0\leqq \alpha_i,\ \beta_i<\nu_i,$$

$$\nu_1\nu_2\cdots\nu_t=n/m,\ \nu_{i+1}/\nu_i,\ i=1,\cdots,t-1;\ a_i^{\nu_i}, b_i^{\nu_i}\in F.$$

THEOREM 19. *The elements $a_1, b_1, \cdots, a_t, b_t$ can be chosen such that*

$$a_i^{\nu_i}=\pm 1,\qquad b_i^{\nu_i}=\pm 1,\qquad i=1,\cdots,t. \tag{4}$$

The proof will be based on the following lemma, which holds for an arbitrary ground field.

LEMMA 17. *Suppose that the group A (see (2)) is represented in the form of a product of two subgroups $A=BC$, where $C\supset F$, $(B, C)=1$.*[10] *Now let C_0 be a normal subgroup of C such that the center of C_0 is contained in F and that C/C_0 is a cyclic group. Then $(A, C)=(C_0, C_0)$.*

PROOF OF THE LEMMA. By assumption,

$$(A, C)=(BC, C)=(C, C).$$

Further, $C=(c)C_0$. Since A is metabelian, $(C, C)=((c)C_0,\ (c)C_0)=((c), C_0)(C_0, C_0)$. Now, if the order of (C_0, C_0) is k, then for $d\in C_0$ we have $d^k\in F_0$, $(d, c)^k=(d^k, c)=1$. Therefore, $(d, c)\in(C_0, C_0)$, $((c_0), C_0)\subseteq(C_0, C_0)$. $(A, C)=(C_0, C_0)$. This proves the lemma. For the case of a finite ground field P we have the following *corollary*: Let $A_0=A\cap \mathrm{SL}(n, P)$, then

$$(A, A)=(A_0, A_0). \tag{5}$$

PROOF OF THE COROLLARY. The correspondence $a\to|a|$, where $a\in A$ and $|a|$ is the determinant of the matrix a, is a homomorphic mapping of A into the multiplicative group of the field P. The kernel of this homomorphism

[10] (B, C) is the commutator group of B and C.

coincides with A_0. On the other hand, the multiplicative group of the finite field P is cyclic. Therefore, A/A_0 is also cyclic. Further, the center Z of A_0 is contained in F, because ZF is an abelian normal subgroup of Γ. When we now take in the conditions of Lemma 17, $B=1$, $C=A$, $C_0=A_0$, we obtain the required corollary.

Let us now proceed to the proof of Theorem 19. If $F=(f)$, then $a_1, b_1, \cdots, a_t, b_t, f$ is a system of generators of A. If we set $B=(a_1)(b_1)\cdots(a_{j-1})(b_{j-1})$, $C=(a_j)(b_j)\cdots(a_t)(b_t)(f)$, then

$$A=BC. \tag{6}$$

The set of all elements of C satisfying the condition

$$x^{\nu i}=\pm 1 \tag{7}$$

will be denoted by C_0. If we can establish that B, C and C_0 satisfy the conditions of Lemma 17 for every j ($j=1,\cdots,t$), then the theorem will be proved.

For arbitrary c_1, c_2 of C we can write

$$(c_1,c_2)=\lambda\in F, \qquad (c_1,c_2)^{\nu j}=1, \qquad (c_2,c_1)^{\nu j}=\lambda^{\rho}c_2^{\nu j}c_1^{\nu j},$$

$$\rho=\frac{\nu_j(\nu_j-1)}{2}$$

Hence,

$$(c_2\, c_1)^{\nu j}=\pm c_2^{\nu j}c_1^{\nu j}. \tag{8}$$

Now if c_1 and c_2 belong to C_0, then it is clear from (8) that c_1c_2 also belongs to C_0. Therefore, C_0 is a normal subgroup of C. From the same equation it is clear that all elements of the form $\pm c^{\nu j}$, where $c\in C$, form a certain subgroup F_1 of F. Let us show that C/C_0 is cyclic. Suppose that $F_1=(f_1)$, $f_1=\pm c_1^{\nu j}$, $c_1\in C$. If $c\in C$, then $c^{\nu j}=f_1^{\alpha}$. Setting $c=c_1^{\alpha}d$ we find that $c^{\nu j}=\pm c_1^{\alpha\nu j}d^{\nu j}=\pm f_1^{\alpha}d^{\nu j}$. Hence $d^{j}=\pm 1$, $d\in C_0$, $c=(c_1)C_0$. Therefore, the factor-group C/C_0 is cyclic. It remains to show that the center of C_0 is contained in F. Suppose, to begin with, that $j=1$, i.e., $C=A$. Obviously, C_0 is a normal subgroup of Γ. If Z is the center of C_0, then ZF is an abelian normal subgroup of Γ. Therefore, $Z\subset F$. Thus B, C and C_0 satisfy for $j=1$ the conditions of Lemma 17. Consequently, we can choose the first pair of generators such that $a_1^{\nu_1}=\pm 1$, $b_1^{\nu_1}=\pm 1$.

Suppose now that for the first $j-1$ pairs $a_1, b_1, \cdots, a_{j-1}, b_{j-1}$ the conditions $a_1^{\nu_1}=\pm 1,\ b_1^{\nu_1}=\pm 1, \cdots, a_{j-1}^{\nu_{j-1}}=\pm 1,\ b_{j-1}^{\nu_{j-1}}=\pm 1$ are satisfied. We examine the group D consisting of all elements of A that satisfy the equation $x^{\nu_j}=\pm 1$.

The group D is a normal subgroup of Γ. Therefore, the center of D is contained in F. Obviously, $D \supset C_0$. Suppose that $d=a_1^{\alpha_1} b_1^{\beta_1} \cdots a_{j-1}^{\alpha_{j-1}} b_{j-1}^{j-1} c$, where $c \in C$, is an element of D. Then we obtain from the condition $d^{\nu_j}=\pm 1$

$$\alpha_i \nu_j \equiv \beta_i \nu_j \equiv 0 \ (\mathrm{mod}\ \nu_i) \qquad i=1, \cdots, j-1. \tag{9}$$

Further,

$$d^{\nu_j}=\epsilon_1^{\gamma_1} \cdots \epsilon_{j-1}^{\gamma_{j-1}} a_1^{\alpha_1 \nu_j} b_1^{\beta_1 \nu_j} \cdots b_{j-1}^{\beta_{j-1} \nu_j}, \qquad c^{\nu_j}=\pm 1,$$

where

$$\gamma_i=-(1/2)\alpha_i \beta_i \nu_i(\nu_i-1).$$

Hence, by using equation (9), we obtain $c^{\nu_j}=\pm 1$, i.e.,

$$c \in C_0, \qquad d=bc, \tag{10}$$

where $b \in B,\ c \in C_0$.

From the last equation and the relation $D \supset C_0$ it follows that the center of C_0 is contained in the center of D. Therefore, the center of C_0 is contained in F. The conditions of Lemma 17 are satisfied and the theorem is proved.

Observe that in the case of an odd ν_i the pair of generators a_i, b_i can be chosen so that $a_i^{\nu_i}=b_i^{\nu_i}=1$. Further, we may always assume that $a_i^{\nu_i}=b_i^{\nu_i}=\pm 1$. For if ν_i is odd, then $a_i^{\nu_i}=b_i^{\nu_i}=1$. Now let ν_i be even and suppose that $a_i^{\nu_i}=-1,\ b_i^{\nu_i}=+1$. Then instead of a_i we take the product $a_i b_i$,

$$(a_i b_i)^{\nu_i}=\epsilon_1^{\pi_i} a_i^{\nu_i} b_i^{\nu_i}=-a_i^{\nu_i}=1, \qquad \pi_i=\frac{\nu_i(1-\nu_i)}{2}.$$

Theorem 19 enables us to reduce the matrices $a_1,\ b_1, \cdots, a_t, b_t$ to a very simple form.

We first consider the case when all the a_i, b_i are subject to the conditions:

$$\begin{gathered} a_1^{\nu_1}=b_1^{\nu_1}=\cdots=a_t^{\nu_t}=b_t^{\nu_t}=1 \\ (a_i, b_i)=\epsilon_i, \quad (a_i, a_j)=(b_i, a_j)=(b_i, b_j)=1. \end{gathered} \tag{11}$$

It is easy to verify that the following t pairs of matrices:

$$c_1, d_1, \cdots, c_t, d_t$$

$$c_i = E_{\nu_1 \cdots \nu_{i-1}} \times \begin{pmatrix} 1 & & & \\ & \epsilon_i & & \\ & & \ddots & \\ & & & \epsilon_i^{\nu_i - 1} \end{pmatrix} \times E_{n/(\nu_1 \nu_2 \cdots \nu_i)},$$

$$d_i = E_{\nu_i \cdots \nu_{i-1}} \times \begin{pmatrix} 0 & 0 & \cdots & 1 \\ 1 & 0 & \cdots & 0 \\ 0 & 1 & \cdots & 0 \\ \cdot & \cdot & \cdots & \cdot \\ \cdot & \cdot & \cdots & \cdot \\ 0 & 0 & \cdots & 0 \end{pmatrix} \times E_{n/\nu_1 \nu_2 \cdots \nu_i}, \quad (12)$$

where E_p is the unit matrix of order p, are also subject to the conditions (11). Therefore, the group $\overline{A} = (c_1)(d_1) \cdots (d_t)F$ is isomorphic to A. The isomorphism between $\overline{A}$ and A can be extended to an automorphism

$$\sum \lambda_{\alpha_1 \cdots \beta_t} c_1^{\alpha_1} \cdots d_t^{\beta_t} \to \sum \lambda_{\alpha_1 \cdots \beta_t} a_1^{\alpha_1} \cdots b_t^{\beta_t}, \quad \lambda_{\alpha_1 \cdots \beta_t} \in K$$

of the algebra $[\overline{A}] = [A] = K_r$, where $[A]$ is the K-hull of A.

Therefore, $\mathrm{GL}(r, K)$ contains a matrix T such that $TA_iT^{-1} = c_i$, $Tb_iT^{-1} = d_i$, $i = 1, \cdots, t$. Thus, if n/m is an odd number, we may assume that the generators a_i, b_i are reduced to the form (12). Suppose now that n/m is even and that for certain ν_i we have $a_i^{\nu_i} = b_i^{\nu_i} = -1$.

Then we set the t pairs of matrices $a_1, b_1, \cdots, a_t, b_t$ in correspondence with the t pairs of matrices $c_1, d_1, \cdots, c_t, d_t$, where c_i and d_i coincide with the matrices (12) for $a_i^{\nu_i} = b_i^{\nu_i} = 1$ and are given by the following formulas (13) if $a_i^{\nu_i} = b_i^{\nu_i} = -1$:

$$c_i = E_{\nu_1 \cdots \nu_{i-1}} \times \begin{bmatrix} \alpha & & & \\ & \alpha^3 & & \\ & & \ddots & \\ & & & \alpha^{\nu_i - 1} \end{bmatrix} \times E_{n/(\nu_1 \cdots \nu_i)},$$

$$d_i = E_{\nu_1 \cdots \nu_{i-1}} \times \begin{bmatrix} 0 & 0 & \cdots & \beta \\ E_2 & 0 & \cdots & 0 \\ 0 & E_2 & \cdots & 0 \\ \cdot & \cdot & \cdots & \cdot \\ \cdot & \cdot & \cdots & \cdot \\ 0 & 0 & \cdots & 0 \end{bmatrix} \times E_{n/(\nu_1 \cdots \nu_i)}, \quad (13)$$

where

$$\alpha = \begin{bmatrix} 0 & \epsilon_i \\ 1 & 0 \end{bmatrix}, \qquad \beta = \begin{bmatrix} \gamma & -\epsilon_i \delta \\ \delta & -\gamma \end{bmatrix},$$

$$\gamma^2-\epsilon_i\delta^2=-1, \qquad \gamma,\delta\in K=\mathrm{GF}(p^{ml}).$$

As in the preceding case it is easy to verify that $\bar{A}=(f)(c_1)(d_1)\cdots(d_t)$ is conjugate to A in $\mathrm{GL}(r,K)$.

3. **Maximal irreducible soluble subgroups of** $\mathrm{GL}(q,p)$, **where** q **and** p **are prime numbers.** Let Γ be one of the maximal irreducible soluble subgroups of $\mathrm{GL}(q,p)$. Three cases are possible:

(a) Γ is imprimitive.

(b) Γ is primitive and the maximal abelian normal subgroup F of Γ is the multiplicative group of the field $K=\mathrm{GF}(p^q)$.

(c) Γ is primitive and the maximal abelian normal subgroup F of Γ coincides with the multiplicative group of the field $P=\mathrm{GF}(p)$.

(a) In this case the space $P^{(q)}$ has a basis $u_1,u_2,\cdots,u_q$ such that for every $g\in\Gamma$

$$g(u_1)=\lambda_1u_{i_1}, g(u_2)=\lambda_2u_{i_2},\cdots,g(u_q)=\lambda_qu_{i_q},$$

where $\lambda_j\in\mathrm{GF}(p)$, $\lambda_j\neq0$, and the permutation $S=\begin{pmatrix}1 & \cdots & q\\ i_1 & \cdots & i_q\end{pmatrix}$ belongs to the full metacyclic group of degree q and of order $q(q-1)$. The order of Γ is $(p-1)^qq(q-1)$ and Γ is now completely determined. For $p=2$ the case (a) cannot occur.

(b) From (1) it follows that Γ has the order $(p^q-1)q$. The space $P^{(q)}$ in which Γ acts can be identified with the field $K=\mathrm{GF}(p^q)$ and the elements g of Γ can be given by the equations

$$g(\xi)=\lambda\xi^{p^u} \qquad 0\leqq u<q, \qquad \lambda,\xi\in\mathrm{GF}(p^q), \qquad \lambda\neq0.$$

(c) The group Γ has the following normal series

$$\Gamma\supset A\supset F\supset E,$$

F is the multiplicative group of a field $\mathrm{GF}(p)$, A/F is a group of order q^2, the elements $a\in A$ have the form

$$a=fa^\alpha b^\beta,\quad f\in F,\quad 0\leqq\alpha,\beta<q,\quad (a,b)=\epsilon,\quad \epsilon^q=1,\quad \epsilon\neq1,\quad \epsilon\in F. \tag{14}$$

The group Γ/A is isomorphic to the soluble group of matrices of the form

$$\begin{bmatrix}\alpha & \beta\\ \gamma & \delta\end{bmatrix}, \qquad \alpha\delta-\beta\gamma=1 \qquad \alpha,\beta,\gamma,\delta\in\mathrm{GF}(q)$$

(see Chapter I, §5). For $g\in\Gamma$

$$g^{-1}ag=f_1a^{\alpha}b^{\beta},$$
$$g^{-1}bg=f_2a^{\gamma}b^{\delta}.$$

When g ranges over the whole group Γ, the matrices (15) range over an irreducible subgroup U of $SL(2,q)$.

In fact, when all the matrices U are simultaneously reduced to the form $\begin{bmatrix}\alpha & 0\\ \gamma & \delta\end{bmatrix}$, then Γ has an abelian normal subgroup of the form (a) $F\supset F$. But this is impossible.

The case (c) can only arise when

$$q/(p-1).$$

To begin with let $q=2$. By Theorem 19, a and b in (14) can be chosen so that

$$a^2=b^2=\pm 1. \tag{16}$$

We examine separately the two possible cases:

1. $p\equiv 1 \pmod 4$, 2. $p\equiv 3 \pmod 4$.

Suppose that $p\equiv 1 \pmod 4$. Then $GF(p)$ contains an element i satisfying the condition $i^2=-1$. Therefore, we may assume that $a^2=b^2=1$.

Hence, it follows that a and b can be simultaneously reduced to the form

$$a=\begin{bmatrix}1 & 0\\ 0 & -1\end{bmatrix},\qquad b=\begin{bmatrix}0 & 1\\ 1 & 0\end{bmatrix}. \tag{17}$$

For $g\in\Gamma$ we have

$$\begin{matrix} g^{-1}ag=\lambda a^{\alpha}b^{\beta} \\ g^{-1}bg=\mu a^{\gamma}b^{\delta}\end{matrix}\qquad \lambda,\mu\in GF(p)\quad 0\leqq\alpha,\ \ \beta<2. \tag{18}$$

$$\alpha\delta-\beta\gamma\equiv 1 \pmod 2.$$

Then, since $a^2=b^2=E_2$,

$$\lambda^2=(-1)^{\alpha\beta},\qquad \mu^2=(-1)^{\gamma\delta}. \tag{19}$$

Γ/A is isomorphic to $GL(2,2)$. $GL(2,2)$ is of order $(2^2-1)(2^2-2)=6$ and is generated by the two elements[11]

$$s=\begin{bmatrix}0 & 1\\ 1 & 1\end{bmatrix},\qquad t=\begin{bmatrix}0 & 1\\ 1 & 0\end{bmatrix}.$$

[11] $GL(2,2)\cong S_3$.

Therefore, to determine Γ it is sufficient to find two matrices g and h satisfying the conditions

$$\begin{aligned} g^{-1}ag&=\lambda b \qquad & h^{-1}ah&=\lambda_1 b \\ g^{-1}bg&=\mu ab \qquad & h^{-1}bh&=\mu_1 a. \end{aligned} \tag{20}$$

By (19) we may assume that $\lambda=\lambda_1=\mu_1=1$, $\mu=i$.

From (20) we find

$$g=\begin{bmatrix} 1 & 1 \\ -i & i \end{bmatrix}, \qquad h=\begin{bmatrix} 1 & 1 \\ 1 & -1 \end{bmatrix}. \tag{21}$$

The group Γ is now completely determined and is of order $24(p-1)$. As generators of Γ we can take the matrices

$$a=\begin{bmatrix} 1 & 0 \\ 0 & -1 \end{bmatrix}, \quad b=\begin{bmatrix} 0 & 1 \\ 1 & 0 \end{bmatrix}, \quad g=\begin{bmatrix} 1 & 1 \\ -i & i \end{bmatrix}, \quad h=\begin{bmatrix} 1 & 1 \\ 1 & -1 \end{bmatrix}, \quad f, \tag{22}$$

where $(f)=F$.

Now suppose that $p\equiv 3 \pmod 4$. By Lemma 17 (see also the corollary) a and b can be chosen so that $|a|=|b|=1$. Since $a^2, b^2\in F$, x^2+1 is the minimal polynomial of a and b. Therefore, the matrix a can be reduced to the form

$$a=\begin{bmatrix} 0 & -1 \\ 1 & 0 \end{bmatrix}.$$

Then we obtain from the conditions $(a, b)=b^2=-1$ that $b=\begin{bmatrix} \alpha & \beta \\ \beta & -\alpha \end{bmatrix}$, $\alpha^2+\beta^2+1=0$, $\alpha, \beta\in \mathrm{GF}(p)$ (compare with (13)). As in the preceding case we now find matrices g and h from the conditions

$$\begin{aligned} g^{-1}ag&=b \qquad & h^{-1}ah&=b \\ g^{-1}bg&=ab \qquad & h^{-1}bh&=a. \end{aligned} \tag{23}$$

The conditions (23) can be rewritten as

$$\begin{aligned} ag&=gb, \qquad & ah&=hb, \\ bg&=gab, \qquad & bh&=ha. \end{aligned}$$

Hence, the search for the matrices g and h reduces to the solution of two systems of linear homogeneous equations. Solving these systems we obtain

$$g=\begin{bmatrix} \alpha^2-\beta & \alpha\beta-1 \\ \alpha\beta+\alpha+\beta & \beta^2-\alpha \end{bmatrix}, \qquad h=\begin{bmatrix} \alpha & \beta-1 \\ \beta+1 & -\alpha \end{bmatrix}$$

Thus Γ is completely determined and Γ is of order $24(p-1)$.

From (20) and (23) it follows that in both cases $p\equiv 1 \pmod 4$ and $p\equiv 3 \pmod 4$ we have $g^3\in A$, $h^2\in A$.

For $q=2$ our discussion is complete.

Now suppose that $q>2$. As is clear from (15), for the investigation of the case (c) it is necessary to know all the nonconjugate maximal irreducible soluble subgroups of $\mathrm{SL}(2, q)$.

The preceding arguments show that every maximal soluble irreducible subgroup of $\mathrm{GL}(2,q)$ is conjugate in $\mathrm{GL}(2,q)$ to one of the following three groups

$$\begin{aligned} &\Gamma_1 \text{ of order } 2(q-1)^2, && \text{case (a)},\\ &\Gamma_2 \text{ of order } 2(q^2-1), && \text{case (b)},\\ &\Gamma_3 \text{ of order } 24(q-1), && \text{case (c)}. \end{aligned}$$

A maximal irreducible soluble subgroup of $\mathrm{SL}(2,q)$ is the intersection of a maximal irreducible soluble subgroup of $\mathrm{GL}(2,q)$ with $\mathrm{SL}(2,q)$. Therefore, we have to construct the intersections $U_i=\Gamma_i\cap\mathrm{SL}(2,q)$, $i=1,2,3$. Γ_i consists of all the matrices of the form

$$\begin{bmatrix}\lambda_1 & 0\\ 0 & \lambda_2\end{bmatrix}\begin{bmatrix}0 & 1\\ 1 & 0\end{bmatrix}^\tau, \qquad \lambda_1,\lambda_2\in\mathrm{GF}(q),\ \ \lambda_1\lambda_2\neq 0,\ \ \tau=0,1.$$

Therefore U_1 consists of all the matrices of the form

$$\begin{bmatrix}\lambda & 0\\ 0 & (-1)^\tau\lambda^{-1}\end{bmatrix}\begin{bmatrix}0 & 1\\ 1 & 0\end{bmatrix}, \qquad \lambda\in\mathrm{GF}(q),\quad \lambda\neq 0,\quad \tau=0,1.$$

The order of U_1 is equal to $2(q-1)$. Γ_2 consists of the elements g of the form

$$g(\xi)=\lambda\xi^{q^k}, \qquad k=0,1,\ \ \xi,\lambda\in\mathrm{GF}(q^2),\ \ \lambda\neq 0.$$

Γ_2 is generated by the two elements g_0 and l_0, where $g_0(\xi)=\xi^q$, $l_0(\xi)=\mu_1,\xi$, μ_1 an element of order q^2-1 in $\mathrm{GF}(q^2)$. Let us compute the determinants of g_0 and l_0. Suppose that $\rho\in\mathrm{GF}(q^2)$, $\rho\notin\mathrm{GF}(q)$. Then $1,\rho$ is a basis of $\mathrm{GF}(q^2)$, $\rho+\rho^q=\alpha\in\mathrm{GF}(q)$, $g_0(1)=1$, $g_0(\rho)=\alpha-\rho$. Therefore, $|g_0|=-1$. We find the determinant of l_0 by taking as basis of $\mathrm{GL}(q^2)$: 1, μ.

$$l_0(1)=\mu,\ l_0(\mu)=\mu^2=-\mu^{q+1}+(\mu^q+\mu)\mu. \quad |l_0|=\begin{vmatrix}0 & 1\\ -\mu^{q+1} & \mu^q+\mu\end{vmatrix}=\mu^{q+1}.$$

For $\lambda\in\mathrm{GF}(q^2)$ we have $\lambda=\mu^t$. If $l(\xi)=\lambda\xi$, then $l=l^t$, $|l|=|l_0|^t=\mu^{t(q+1)}=\lambda^{q+1}$. Obviously, $g=lg_0^k$. If $|g|=1$, then $(-1)^k\lambda^{q+1}=1$. So the group U_2 has been found. The order of U_2 is equal to $2(q+1)$.

Now we examine Γ_3 and U_3. We have seen that Γ_3 is generated by the elements f, a, b, g, h. The determinants $|f|, |a|, |b|$ are quadratic residues modulo q. Further, $g^3 \in A$. Therefore, $|g|$ is also a quadratic residue. Now let us clarify this for $|h|$.

For $q \equiv 1 \pmod 4$,

$$h = \begin{bmatrix} 1 & 1 \\ 1 & -1 \end{bmatrix} \qquad |h| = -2.$$

If $q \equiv 3 \pmod 4$, then

$$h = \begin{bmatrix} \alpha & \beta - 1 \\ \beta + 1 & -\alpha \end{bmatrix}, \qquad \alpha^2 + \beta^2 + 1 = 0.$$

Hence $|h| = 2$. Thus, for the Legendre symbol $\left(\frac{|h|}{q}\right)$ we can write in both cases

$$\left(\frac{|h|}{q}\right) = \left(\frac{2}{q}\right).$$

Therefore, for $q \equiv \pm 1 \pmod 8$ $|h|$ is a quadratic residue and all the determinants of the matrices of Γ_3 are quadratic residues. In that case the determinants of the matrices of Γ_3 form a group of order $(q-1)/2$. Therefore, for $q \equiv \pm 1 \pmod 8$ the order of U_3 is 48.

For $q \equiv \pm 3 \pmod 8$, $\left(\frac{|h|}{q}\right) = -1$, the determinants of the matrices of Γ_3 form a group of order $q-1$. The order of U_3 is 24.

Thus we have found the intersections of Γ_1, Γ_2, Γ_3 with $\mathrm{SL}(2,q)$. However, we have to take into account that when Γ is conjugate to Γ' in $\mathrm{GL}(2,q)$, it does not always follow that $\Gamma \cap \mathrm{SL}(2,q)$ is conjugate to $\Gamma' \cap \mathrm{SL}(2,q)$ in $\mathrm{SL}(2,q)$. Therefore a group Γ that is conjugate to Γ_i in $\mathrm{GL}(2,q)$ may, in general, give an intersection with $\mathrm{SL}(2,q)$ that is not conjugate to U_i in $\mathrm{SL}(2,q)$.

Let us examine this problem in more detail. If the determinants of the matrices of $\Gamma \subset \mathrm{GL}(n,P)$ form a group that coincides with the multiplicative group of the field P, then conjugacy of Γ' and Γ in $\mathrm{GL}(n,P)$ implies the conjugacy of $\Gamma' \cap \mathrm{SL}(n,P)$ with $\Gamma \cap \mathrm{SL}(n,P)$ in $\mathrm{SL}(n,P)$. For suppose that

$$T^{-1}\Gamma T = \Gamma, \qquad T \in \mathrm{GL}(n,P).$$

By assumption, Γ contains a matrix R such that $|R| = |T|^{-1}$. Obviously, if $C = RT$, then $C^{-1}\Gamma C = \Gamma'$, $C \in \mathrm{SL}(n,P)$.

Therefore, $\Gamma' \cap \mathrm{SL}(n,P)$ is conjugate with $\Gamma \cap \mathrm{SL}(n,P)$ in $\mathrm{SL}(n,P)$.

The determinants of the matrices of Γ_1 and Γ_2 always form a group of order $q-1$ and so do those of Γ_3 for $q \equiv \pm 3 \pmod 8$. Therefore, it remains to consider the case of the group Γ_3 for $q \equiv \pm 1 \pmod 8$. In that case the class of subgroups of $\mathrm{GL}(2,q)$ that are conjugate to Γ_3 yields two classes of conjugate subgroups of $\mathrm{SL}(2,q)$. (a) The class of subgroups of $\mathrm{SL}(2,q)$ conjugate to $U_3 = \Gamma_3 \cap \mathrm{SL}(2,q)$ in $\mathrm{SL}(2,q)$; (b) the class of subgroups of $\mathrm{SL}(2,q)$ conjugate to $U_3' = T^{-1}U_3T$, where $|T|$ is a quadratic nonresidue modulo q. Thus, for $q>2$ the group $\mathrm{GL}(q,P)$ cannot have more than six nonconjugate maximal soluble irreducible subgroups:

1. $\Gamma^{(1)}$ of order $q(q-1)(p-1)^q$, (a)
2. $\Gamma^{(2)}$ of order $q(p^q-1)$, (b)
3. $\Gamma^{(3)}$ of order $2(p-1)(q-1)q^2$,
4. $\Gamma^{(4)}$ of order $2(p-1)(q+1)q^2$,
5. $\Gamma^{(5)}$ (i) $q \equiv \pm 1 \pmod 8$, $\Gamma^{(5)}$ of order $48(p-1)q^2$, (ii) $q \equiv \pm 3 \pmod 8$, $\Gamma^{(5)}$ of order $24(p-1)q^2$,
6. $\Gamma^{(6)}$ of order $48(p-1)q^2$, $q \equiv \pm 1 \pmod 8$.

The groups $\Gamma^{(3)}$, $\Gamma^{(4)}$, $\Gamma^{(5)}$, $\Gamma^{(6)}$ occur only when $q/p-1$. A necessary condition for the occurrence of $\Gamma^{(6)}$ is

$$q \equiv \pm 1 \pmod 8.$$

$\Gamma^{(3)}$, $\Gamma^{(4)}$, $\Gamma^{(5)}$, $\Gamma^{(6)}$ have a normal subgroup A of order $(p-1)q^2$. The matrices of A are of the form

$$a = f a_1^{\alpha} b_1^{\beta}, \qquad f \in F, \ 0 \leqq \alpha, \ \beta < q$$

$$a_1 = \begin{bmatrix} 1 & & & & \\ & \epsilon & & & \\ & & \epsilon^2 & & \\ & & & \ddots & \\ & & & & \epsilon^{q-1} \end{bmatrix}, \qquad b_1 = \begin{bmatrix} 0 & 0 & \cdots & 0 & 1 \\ 1 & 0 & \cdots & 0 & 0 \\ 0 & 1 & \cdots & 0 & 0 \\ \cdot & \cdot & \cdots & \cdot & \cdot \\ \cdot & \cdot & \cdots & \cdot & \cdot \\ 0 & 0 & \cdots & 1 & 0 \end{bmatrix},$$

$$\epsilon \in \mathrm{GF}(p), \ \epsilon^q = 1, \ \epsilon \neq 1.$$

$\Gamma^{(3)}$, $\Gamma^{(4)}$, $\Gamma^{(5)}$ are uniquely determined by A and the groups U_1, U_2, U_3, respectively. $\Gamma^{(6)}$ is uniquely determined by the groups A and U_3'.

It is easy to list the cases when all the maximal irreducible soluble subgroups of $\mathrm{GL}(p,q)$ are conjugate in $\mathrm{GL}(p,q)$:

1. $p=2$, q is an arbitrary prime number;
2. $p=3$, $q=2$.

In the first case all the maximal soluble irreducible subgroups of $\mathrm{GL}(p,q)$ are conjugate to the group $\Gamma^{(2)}$ of order $q(2^q-1)$.

In the second case the whole group $\mathrm{GL}(p,q)$ is soluble.

The results of this section were obtained in [**14**]. It should be mentioned that in [**14**] the existence of the group U_3' was ignored. On the other hand, the group $\mathfrak{G}^{(3)}$ (in the notation of [**14**]) is not maximal, because it is contained in $\mathfrak{G}^{(2)}$.

4. Maximal soluble subgroups of $\mathrm{GL}(n,P)$, where P is an algebraically closed field.

1. If P is an algebraically closed field and $\mathrm{GL}(n,P)$ has primitive soluble subgroups, then by Theorem 12 the characteristic of P cannot be a divisor of n.

Now let G be a maximal primitive soluble subgroup of $\mathrm{GL}(n,P)$, where P is an algebraically closed field. Then a maximal abelian normal subgroup F of G coincides with the multiplicative group of the field PE_n (see Theorem 1).

Obviously, the centralizer of F in G coincides with G and in accordance with results of Chapter I, G has a normal series of the form

$$G\supset A\supset F\supset E,$$

where A/F is a maximal abelian normal subgroup of the factor-group G/F, $A:F=n^2$, and the linear P-hull $[A]$ of A coincides with P_n.

A can be represented in the form

$$A=(a_1)(b_1)\cdots(a_t)(b_t)F,$$

$$(a_i,b_i)=\epsilon_i E_n,\quad (a_i,a_j)=(a_i,b_j)=(b_i,b_j)=E_n, \tag{24}$$

where ϵ_i is a primitive root of the equation $x^{\nu_i}=1$, $\nu_1\nu_2\cdots\nu_t=n$, ν_{i+1}/ν_i, ν_i is square-free, $a_i^{\nu_i}\in F$, $b_i^{\nu_i}\in F$.

Since P is algebraically closed, P contains elements λ_i and μ_i such that $(\lambda_i a_i)^{\nu_i}=(\mu_i b_i)^{\nu_i}=E_n$. Therefore, we may assume that the elements a_i and b_i are subject to the conditions

$$a_i^{\nu_i}=b_i^{\nu_i}=E_n,\qquad i=1,2,\cdots,t. \tag{25}$$

But as is easy to verify, the t pairs of matrices

$$a_i' = E_{\nu_1\nu_2\cdots\nu_{i-1}} \times \begin{bmatrix} 1 & & & \\ & \epsilon_i & & \\ & & \ddots & \\ & & & \epsilon_i^{\nu_i-1} \end{bmatrix} \times E_{n/(\nu_1\cdots\nu_i)},$$

$$b_i' = E_{\nu_1\nu_2\cdots\nu_{i-1}} \times \begin{bmatrix} 0 & 0 & \cdots & 1 \\ 1 & 0 & \cdots & 0 \\ 0 & 1 & \cdots & 0 \\ \cdot & \cdot & \cdots & \cdot \\ \cdot & \cdot & \cdots & \cdot \\ 0 & 0 & \cdots & 0 \end{bmatrix} \times E_{n/(\nu_1\cdots\nu_i)} \qquad (26)$$

satisfy the conditions (24) and (25). Therefore the groups A and $A' = (a_1')(b_1')\cdots(a_t')(b_t')F$ are isomorphic, and the isomorphism $a_1^{\alpha_1}b_1^{\beta_1}\cdots a_t^{\alpha_t}b_t^{\beta_t} \to a_1'^{\alpha_1}b_1'^{\beta_1}\cdots a_t'^{\alpha_t}b_t'^{\beta_t}$ can be extended to an automorphism

$$\sum \lambda_{\alpha_1\cdots\beta_t} a_1^{\alpha_1}\cdots b_t^{\beta_t} \to \sum \lambda_{\alpha_1\cdots\beta_t}\ a_1'^{\alpha_1}\cdots b_t'^{\beta_t},\quad \lambda_{\alpha_1\cdots\beta_t} \in P$$

of the algebra $[A] = [A'] = P_n$.

Thus $\mathrm{GL}(n,P)$ contains a matrix T such that $T^{-1}a_i T = a_i'$, $T^{-1}b_i T = b_i'$, $i = 1, \cdots, t$.

In view of this we may assume that a_i and b_i coincide with a_i' and b_i', respectively. Hence, it follows that the group A is uniquely determined to within conjugacy in $\mathrm{GL}(n,P)$ by the number n and the field P.

2. Now let $n = q_1^{l_1} q_2^{l_2} \cdots q_k^{l_k}$ be the canonical decomposition of n; using the formulae (35) of Chapter I we can then reduce the group A to the form

$$A = (a_{11})(b_{11})\cdots(a_{1l_1})(b_{1l_1})\cdots(a_{k1})(b_{k1})\cdots(a_{kl_k})(b_{kl_k})F, \qquad (27)$$

$$a_{11} = \begin{bmatrix} 1 & 0 & \cdots & 0 \\ 0 & \eta_1 & \cdots & 0 \\ \cdot & \cdot & \cdots & \cdot \\ \cdot & \cdot & \cdots & \cdot \\ 0 & 0 & \cdots & \eta_1^{q_1-1} \end{bmatrix} \times E_{n/q_1}, \qquad b_{11} = \begin{bmatrix} 0 & 0 & \cdots & 0 & 1 \\ 1 & 0 & \cdots & 0 & 0 \\ 0 & 1 & \cdots & 0 & 0 \\ \cdot & \cdot & \cdots & \cdot & \cdot \\ \cdot & \cdot & \cdots & \cdot & \cdot \\ 0 & 0 & \cdots & 1 & 0 \end{bmatrix} \times E_{n/q_1},$$

$$a_{12} = E_{q_1} \times \begin{bmatrix} 1 & 0 & \cdots & 0 \\ 0 & \eta_1 & \cdots & 0 \\ \cdot & \cdot & \cdots & \cdot \\ \cdot & \cdot & \cdots & \cdot \\ 0 & 0 & \cdots & \eta_1^{q_1-1} \end{bmatrix} E_{n/(q_1q_2)}, \qquad b_{12} = E_{q_1} \times \begin{bmatrix} 0 & 0 & \cdots & 0 & 1 \\ 1 & 0 & \cdots & 0 & 0 \\ 0 & 1 & \cdots & 0 & 0 \\ \cdot & \cdot & \cdots & \cdot & \cdot \\ \cdot & \cdot & \cdots & \cdot & \cdot \\ 0 & 0 & \cdots & 1 & 0 \end{bmatrix} \times E_{n/(q_1q_2)},$$

. . . .

$$a_{k1}=E_{n/q_k^{l_k}}\times\begin{bmatrix}1&0&\cdots&0\\0&\eta_k&\cdots&0\\\cdot&\cdot&\cdots&\cdot\\\cdot&\cdot&\cdots&\cdot\\0&0&\cdots&\eta_k^{q_k-1}\end{bmatrix}\times E_{q_k^{l_k-1}},\quad b_{k1}=E_{n/q_k^{l_k}}\times\begin{bmatrix}0&0&\cdots&0&1\\1&0&\cdots&0&0\\0&1&\cdots&0&0\\\cdot&\cdot&\cdots&\cdot&\cdot\\\cdot&\cdot&\cdots&\cdot&\cdot\\0&0&\cdots&1&0\end{bmatrix}\times E_{q_k^{l_k-1}},$$

. . . .

. . . .

$$a_{kl_k}=E_{n/q_k}\times\begin{bmatrix}1&0&\cdots&0\\0&\eta_k&\cdots&0\\\cdot&\cdot&\cdots&\cdot\\\cdot&\cdot&\cdots&\cdot\\0&0&\cdots&\eta_k^{q_k-1}\end{bmatrix},\qquad b_{kl_k}=E_{n/q_k}\times\begin{bmatrix}0&0&\cdots&0&1\\1&0&\cdots&0&0\\0&1&\cdots&0&0\\\cdot&\cdot&\cdots&\cdot&\cdot\\\cdot&\cdot&\cdots&\cdot&\cdot\\0&0&\cdots&1&0\end{bmatrix},$$

$$\eta_i\in P,\quad \eta_i^{q_i}=1,\quad \eta_i\neq 1,\quad i=1,2,\cdots,k.$$

The matrices a_{ij}, b_{ij} satisfy the following conditions:

$$(a_{ij},b_{ij})=\eta_i$$
$$(a_{ij},a_{\mu\nu})=(a_{ij},b_{\mu\nu})=(b_{ij},b_{\mu\nu})=1, \qquad (\alpha)$$

if

$$(i-\mu)^2+(j-\nu)^2\neq 0,\qquad a_{ij}^{q_i}=b_{ij}^{q_i}=E_n. \qquad (\beta)$$

By Theorem 11, G/A is isomorphic to a certain soluble subgroup of the direct product of the k symplectic groups

$$S_p(2l_1,q_1),\cdots,S_p(2l_k,q_k).$$

We can show that G/A is isomorphic to the direct product of k maximal soluble subgroups $\Gamma_{01},\Gamma_{02},\cdots,\Gamma_{0k}$ of the symplectic groups $S_p(2l_1,q_1),\cdots,S_p(2l_k,q_k)$.

For if a'_{ij}, b'_{ij} belong to A and are subject to the conditions (i) and (ii), then $\mathrm{GL}(n,P)$ contains an element c such that $c^{-1}a_{ij}c=a'_{ij}$, $c^{-1}b_{ij}c=b'_{ij}$.

But the condition (i) guarantees that the elements a'_{ij}, b'_{ij} determine k symplectic matrices $S_1,\cdots,S_k$ of $S_p(2l_1,q_1),\cdots,S_p(2l_k,q_k)$ (see (40) of Chapter I).

If a'_{ij}, b'_{ij} satisfy the condition (i), then $a'^{q_i}_{ij}\in PE_n$, $b'^{q_i}_{ij}\in PE_n$. Since P is an algebraically closed field, we can achieve that conditions (ii) are satisfied, multiplying if necessary by elements of P. But then our assertion follows. Since A is uniquely determined by the field P and the number n to within conjugacy in $\mathrm{GL}(n,P)$, and Γ is completely given by A and the groups

$\Gamma_{0i} \subseteq S_p(2l_i, q_i)$, $\mathrm{GL}(n, P)$ contains only a finite number of *nonconjugate maximal primitive soluble subgroups*.

If the characteristic of P is zero or is prime to n, then $\mathrm{GL}(n, P)$ contains primitive soluble subgroups.

For in this case P contains for every prime divisor q of n a primitive root of the equation $x^q = 1$.

Therefore we can construct the group A by the formula (27). On the other hand, for arbitrary k soluble subgroups $\Gamma_{01}, \cdots, \Gamma_{0k}$ of the symplectic groups $S_p(2l_1, q_1), \cdots, S_p(2l_k, q_k)$ there exists in $\mathrm{GL}(n, P)$ a soluble subgroup $\Gamma \supset A$ such that Γ / A is isomorphic to the direct product of $\Gamma_{01}, \cdots, \Gamma_{0k}$.

By §5, 4. of Chapter I the irreducibility of all the groups Γ_{0i} follows from the primitivity of Γ.

Thus it remains to show the existence of irreducibile soluble subgroups in $S_p(2l_k, q)$.

In §3 we have seen that for $l = 1$ the group $S_p(2l, q)$ contains irreducible soluble subgroups.[12] Let H_0 be an irreducible soluble subgroup of $S_p(2, q)$. We can construct an irreducible soluble subgroup H_0 of $S_p(2l, q)$ as follows: $\Gamma^0 = (g_0) H_0$, where H_0 consists of all the matrices of the form

$$\begin{bmatrix} H_1 & & & \\ & H_2 & & \\ & & \ddots & \\ & & & H_l \end{bmatrix},$$

H_i range over H_0 independently,

$$g_0 = \begin{bmatrix} 0_2 & 0_2 & \cdots & 0_2 & E_2 \\ E_2 & 0_2 & \cdots & 0_2 & 0_2 \\ 0_2 & E_2 & \cdots & 0_2 & 0_2 \\ \cdot & \cdot & \cdots & \cdot & \cdot \\ \cdot & \cdot & \cdots & \cdot & \cdot \\ 0_2 & 0_2 & \cdots & E_2 & 0_2 \end{bmatrix}.$$

Thus if P is algebraically closed, then $\mathrm{GL}(n, P)$ contains primitive soluble subgroups if and only if the characteristic of P is either zero or is prime to n.

3. THEOREM 29. *The full linear group over an algebraically closed field has only a finite number of nonconjugate maximal soluble subgroups.*

PROOF. We have already seen that $\mathrm{GL}(n, P)$ can only contain a finite

[12] We have already mentioned that $S_p(2, q) = \mathrm{SL}(2, q)$.

number of nonconjugate maximal primitive soluble subgroups. Since a maximal irreducible soluble subgroup of $\mathrm{GL}(n, P)$ is determined by a certain maximal primitive soluble subgroup of $\mathrm{GL}(n/k, P)$ and a maximal soluble transitive subgroup of the symmetric group S_k (see Lemma 5 of Chapter I), the theorem is true for irreducible subgroups of $\mathrm{GL}(n, P)$. Furthermore, by §1 of Chapter I every maximal soluble subgroup of $\mathrm{GL}(n, P)$ is determined by its irreducible parts and the order in which they occur. Hence, the theorem follows.

4. EXAMPLE. As an example we consider the maximal irreducible soluble subgroups of $\mathrm{GL}(n, P)$, where P is an algebraically closed field of characteristic zero and n is a square-free number, $n = q_1 q_2 \cdots q_s$, where q_i are distinct prime numbers.

Let Γ be a maximal soluble irreducible subgroup of $\mathrm{GL}(n, P)$. Two cases are possible:

(a) Γ is primitive,

(b) Γ is imprimitive.

(a) Γ has a normal series of the form:

$$\Gamma \supset A \supset F \supset E,$$

where F is the group of scalar nonsingular matrices of order n over P,

$$A = (u_1)(v_1) \cdots (u_s)(v_s) F,$$

$$u_i = E_{q_1 q_2 \cdots q_{i-1}} \times \begin{bmatrix} 1 & & & \\ & \eta_i & & \\ & & \ddots & \\ & & & \eta_i^{q_i - 1} \end{bmatrix} \times E_{n/(q_1 q_2 \cdots q_i)},$$

$$v_i = E_{q_1 q_2 \cdots q_{i-1}} \times \begin{bmatrix} 0 & 0 & \cdots & 0 & 1 \\ 1 & 0 & \cdots & 0 & 0 \\ 0 & 1 & \cdots & 0 & 0 \\ \cdot & \cdot & \cdots & \cdot & \cdot \\ \cdot & \cdot & \cdots & \cdot & \cdot \\ 0 & 0 & \cdots & 1 & 0 \end{bmatrix} \times E_{n/(q_1 q_2 \cdots q_i)}, \qquad \eta_i \in P, \quad \eta_i \neq 1, \quad \eta_i^{q_i} = 1.$$

The elements g of Γ are determined by the conditions

$$g u_i g^{-1} = \lambda_i u_i^{\alpha_i} v_i^{\gamma_i} = u_i'$$

$$g v_i g^{-1} = \mu_i u_i^{\beta_i} v_i^{\delta_i} = v_i'$$

$$\alpha_i, \beta_i, \gamma_i, \delta_i \in \mathrm{GF}(q_i),$$

$$\alpha_i \delta_i - \beta_i \gamma_i = 1, \quad \lambda_i, \mu_i \in P,$$

$$u_i'^{q_i} = v_i'^{q_i} = E_n.$$

The matrices $\begin{bmatrix} \alpha_i & \beta_i \\ \gamma_i & \delta_i \end{bmatrix}$ range over a maximal soluble subgroup Γ_{0i} of the special linear group $\mathrm{SL}(2, q_i) = S_p(2, q_i)$, $i = 1, \cdots, s$.

Let us show that the groups Γ_{0i}, $i = 1, \cdots, s$, are irreducible. Suppose, for example, that Γ_{01} is reducible. Then we may assume that all the matrices of Γ_{01} are of the form

$$\begin{bmatrix} \alpha_1 & \beta_1 \\ 0 & \delta_1 \end{bmatrix},$$

i.e., $g u_1 g^{-1} = \lambda_1 u_1^{\alpha_1}$.

Therefore, $(u_1)F \supset F$ is an abelian normal subgroup of Γ, but this is impossible.

Thus Γ/A is isomorphic to the direct product of the maximal irreducible soluble subgroups $\Gamma_{0i} \subseteq \mathrm{SL}(2, q_i)$. We have already determined the maximal soluble irreducible subgroups of $\mathrm{SL}(2, q)$ (see §3). The group $\mathrm{SL}(2, q)$ has at most 4 nonconjugate maximal soluble subgroups, so that $\mathrm{GL}(n, P)$ contains at most 4^s nonconjugate maximal primitive soluble subgroups.

(b) Γ is imprimitive. Suppose that the complete decomposition of $P^{(n)}$ into systems of imprimitivity of Γ contains r direct summands. Then Γ is determined by a maximal primitive soluble subgroup of $\mathrm{GL}(n/r, P)$ and a maximal soluble transitive subgroup of the symmetric group S_r. Suppose for definiteness that $r = q_1 q_2 \cdots q_k$. Every transitive soluble subgroup H_0 of S_r is imprimitive for $k > 1$. Therefore, H_0 has systems of imprimitivity containing a prime number of symbols. One of the maximal soluble subgroups of S_r is the group $H_{0q_1q_2\cdots q_k}$ of order

$$[q_1(q_1-1)]^{r/q_1} \ [q_2(q_2-1)]^{r/(q_1q_2)} \cdots [q_k(q_k-1)].$$

The group $H_{0q_1q_2\cdots q_k}$ has r/q_1 systems of imprimitivity. On its systems of imprimitivity $H_{0q_1q_2\cdots q_k}$ effects a group of permutations of degree r/q_1 having $n/(q_1q_2)$ systems of imprimitivity etc. All the remaining maximal soluble transitive subgroups of S_r are obtained from $H_{0q_1q_2\cdots q_k}$ by permuting the numbers $q_1, q_2, \cdots, q_k$.

Therefore, S_r contains $k!$ nonconjugate maximal soluble transitive subgroups.

Thus the number of all nonconjugate maximal soluble irreducible subgroups of $\mathrm{GL}(n, P)$ (primitive and imprimitive) does not exceed the number

$$l(s) = \sum_{k=0}^{s} k! \binom{s}{k} 4^{s-k} = \sum_{k=0}^{s} \frac{s!}{(s-k)!} 4^{s-k}.$$

5. THEOREM 21. (A. I. Mal′cev [12].) *Every soluble subgroup of the full linear group over an algebraically closed field has a normal subgroup of finite index whose matrices can be reduced simultaneously to triangular form.*

PROOF. Let Γ be a soluble subgroup of $\mathrm{GL}(n, P)$. By §1 of Chapter I the matrices g of Γ can be reduced simultaneously to a form

$$g=\begin{bmatrix} A_{11}^g & A_{12}^g & \cdots & A_{1k}^g \\ 0 & A_{22}^g & \cdots & A_{2k}^g \\ \cdot & \cdot & \cdots & \cdot \\ \cdot & \cdot & \cdots & \cdot \\ 0 & 0 & \cdots & A_{kk}^g \end{bmatrix},$$

where the mapping $g \rightarrow A_{ii}^g$ is an irreducible representation Γ_i of Γ. The soluble group Γ_i has an abelian normal subgroup F_i of finite index. We reduce the matrices of all F_i, $i=1, \cdots, k$, to diagonal form.

Then all the matrices of Γ assume the form

$$\begin{bmatrix} L_1 & A_{12} & \cdots & A_{1k} \\ 0 & L_2 & \cdots & A_{2k} \\ \cdot & \cdot & \cdots & \cdot \\ \cdot & \cdot & \cdots & \cdot \\ 0 & 0 & \cdots & L_k \end{bmatrix}$$

where the $L_i \in F_i$ form a normal subgroup of Γ of finite index. The theorem is now proved.

5. **Soluble irreducible subgroup of the full linear group over the field of real numbers.** Now let D be the field of real numbers. We examine a maximal primitive soluble subgroup Γ of $\mathrm{GL}(n, D)$. By Theorem 1 two cases are possible:

(a) A maximal abelian normal subgroup F of Γ is the multiplicative group of the field DE_n.

(b) A maximal abelian normal subgroup F is isomorphic to the multiplicative group of the field of complex numbers K.

Case (a). Γ has the normal series

$$\Gamma \supset A \supset F \supset E,$$

$$A=(a_1)(b_1)\cdots(a_t)(b_t)F,$$

$$(a_i, b_i)=\epsilon_i E_n,$$

ϵ_i is a primitive root of the equation $x^{\nu_i}=1$, $\epsilon_i \in D$

$$\nu_1 \nu_2 \cdots \nu_t = n, \quad (a_i, b_j)=(a_i, a_j)=(b_i, b_j)=1.$$

Since the only roots of unity in D are the numbers ± 1, we have $\nu_1 = \nu_2 = \cdots = \nu_t = 2$, $n = 2^t$.

Thus, the case (a) can only occur when $n = 2^t$. Since $\nu_i = 2$, we have $(a_i, b_i) = -E_n$, $i = 1, 2, \cdots, t$, $a_i^2, b_i^2 \in F$. Multiplying a_i and b_i by real numbers we can achieve that the conditions $a_i^2 = b_i^2 = \pm E_n$ are satisfied.

However, the only possible case is $a_1^2 = b_1^2 = \cdots = a_t^2 = b_t^2 = E_n$. For suppose that $a_t^2 = b_t^2 = -E_n$. Then all the remaining pairs a_i, b_i, $i < t$ can be chosen so that $a_i^2 = b_i^2 = E_n$. (If we had an $a_1^2 = b_1^2 = -E_n$, we could replace a_1, b_1 by $a_1' = a_1 a_t$, $b_1' = b_1 b_t$.) From the assumptions $a_1^2 = b_1^2 = E_n$, $(a_1, b_1) = -E_n$ it follows that the matrices a_1 and b_1 can be reduced to the form

$$a_1 = \begin{bmatrix} E_{n/2} & 0 \\ 0 & -E_{n/2} \end{bmatrix}, \qquad b_1 = \begin{bmatrix} 0 & B_1^{-1} \\ B_1 & 0 \end{bmatrix}.$$

It is easy to verify that

$$\begin{bmatrix} E_{n/2} & 0 \\ 0 & B_1 \end{bmatrix}^{-1} \begin{bmatrix} 0 & B_1^{-1} \\ B_1 & 0 \end{bmatrix} \begin{bmatrix} E_{n/2} & 0 \\ 0 & B_1 \end{bmatrix} = \begin{bmatrix} 0 & E_{n/2} \\ E_{n/2} & 0 \end{bmatrix}.$$

Obviously, the matrix a_1 does not change its form under such a transformation. Therefore, we may assume that

$$a_1 = \begin{bmatrix} 1 & 0 \\ 0 & -1 \end{bmatrix} \times E_{n/2}, \qquad b_1 = \begin{bmatrix} 0 & 1 \\ 1 & 0 \end{bmatrix} \times E_{n/2}.$$

Since a_2, b_2 are permutable with a_1 and b_1, they have the form $a_2 = E_2 \times A_2$, $b_2 = E_2 \times B_2$, $(A_2, B_2) = -E_{n/2}$, $A_2^2 = B_2^2 = E_{n/2}$. By means of $E_2 \times C$ we reduce a_2, b_2 to the form

$$a_2 = E_2 \times \begin{bmatrix} 1 & 0 \\ 0 & -1 \end{bmatrix} \times E_{n/2^2},$$

$$b_2 = E_2 \times \begin{bmatrix} 0 & 1 \\ 1 & 0 \end{bmatrix} \times E_{n/2^2}.$$

Continuing this way we obtain for all pairs $a_j, b_j, j < t$, simultaneously

$$\begin{aligned} a_j &= E_{2^{j-1}} \times \begin{bmatrix} 1 & 1 \\ 0 & -1 \end{bmatrix} \times E_{2^{t-j}}, \\ b_j &= E_{2^{j-1}} \times \begin{bmatrix} 0 & 1 \\ 1 & 0 \end{bmatrix} \times E_{2^{t-j}}. \end{aligned} \tag{28}$$

Since a_t and b_t are permutable with all a_j and b_j, $j < t$, we have $a_t = E_{2^{t-1}} \times A_t$, $b_t = E_{2^{t-j}} \times B_t$, $A_t^2 = B_t^2 = -E_2$, $(A_t, B_t) = -E_2$. Obviously, without altering $a_j, b_j, j < t$, the matrix A_t can be reduced to the form $A_t = \begin{bmatrix} 0 & -1 \\ 1 & 0 \end{bmatrix}$. Let $A_t =$

$\begin{bmatrix} 0 & -1 \\ 1 & 0 \end{bmatrix}$, $B_t=\begin{bmatrix} \alpha & \beta \\ \gamma & \delta \end{bmatrix}$. From the condition $(A_t, B_t)=-E_2$ we find $B_t=$ $\begin{bmatrix} \alpha & \beta \\ \beta & -\alpha \end{bmatrix}$. From the equation $B_t^2=-E_2$ we obtain $\begin{bmatrix} \alpha^2+\beta^2 & 0 \\ 0 & \alpha^2+\beta^2 \end{bmatrix}=$ $-E_2$. But the latter is impossible. Thus $a_j^2=b_j^2=E_n$, $j=1, \cdots, t$. Hence it follows that the formulas (28) remain valid for $j=t$. The group A is now completely determined.

The group Γ is contained in the normalizer N of A in $\mathrm{GL}(n, D)$. The index of A in N does not exceed the order of the symplectic group $S_p(2t, 2)$. Therefore, in Case (a) we obtain only a finite number of maximal primitive soluble subgroups of $\mathrm{GL}(n, D)$.

In contrast to the case when the ground field is algebraically closed, it is not true here that to every soluble subgroup Γ_0 of $S_p(2t, 2)$ there corresponds a maximal primitive soluble subgroup of $\mathrm{GL}(n, D)$ with the factor-group Γ/A isomorphic to Γ_0.

For the matrices g of Γ are determined from equations of the form

$$g^{-1}a_i g=\lambda_i a_1^{\alpha_{i1}} b_1^{\beta_{i1}} \cdots a_t^{\alpha_{it}} b_t^{\beta_{it}}=C_i,$$

$$g^{-1}b_i g=\mu_i a_1^{\gamma_{i1}} b_1^{\delta_{i1}} \cdots a_t^{\gamma_{it}} b_t^{\delta_{it}}=d_i.$$

Since $a_i^2=b_i^2=E_n$, $i=1,\cdots,t$, we also have $c_i^2=d_i^2=E_n$. Therefore $\alpha_{ij}, \beta_{ij}, \gamma_{ij}, \delta_{ij}\in\mathrm{GF}(2)$ are subject to the condition

$$\sum_{j=1}^{t} \alpha_{ij}\beta_{ij}=\sum_{j=1}^{t} \gamma_{ij}\delta_{ij}=0, \qquad i=1, 2, \cdots, t. \tag{29}$$

In particular, from (29) it follows that for $n=2$, i.e., for $t=1$, Case (a) is impossible. For it follows from (28) that for $t=1$ the matrix $\begin{bmatrix} \alpha_1 & \beta_1 \\ \gamma_1 & \delta_1 \end{bmatrix}$ is either equal to E_2 or is $\begin{bmatrix} 0 & 1 \\ 1 & 0 \end{bmatrix}$. Consequently, for every $g\in\Gamma$ we have $g^{-1}a_1 b_1 g=a_1 b_1$, but this contradicts the primitivity of Γ.

Case (b). Since $K:D=2$, $n=2r$. If $r>1$, then Γ has the series

$$\Gamma\supseteq V\supset A\supset F\supset E,$$

where F is isomorphic to the multiplicative group of K. The matrices of the group can be written in the form

$$E_2\times\begin{bmatrix} \lambda & -\mu \\ \mu & \lambda \end{bmatrix}, \qquad \lambda, \mu\in D, \qquad \lambda^2+\mu^2\neq 0.$$

The matrices of V can be regarded as matrices of order r whose elements are matrices of order 2

$$\begin{bmatrix} \lambda & -\mu \\ \mu & \lambda \end{bmatrix} = \tau, \qquad \lambda, \mu \in D.$$

Obviously, the matrices τ form a field $K' \cong K$. For the construction of A it is sufficient to write down the decomposition of $n/2 = r = \nu_1 \nu_2 \cdots \nu_t$, where ν_{j+1}/ν_j, $j = 1, 2, \cdots, t-1$, and all the ν_j are square-free. $A = (a_1)(b_1) \cdots (a_t)(b_t)F$, where the matrices a_j, b_j over a field K' have the form

$$a_j = E_{\nu_1 \nu_2 \dots \nu_{j-1}} \times \begin{bmatrix} e & & & \\ & \epsilon_j & & \\ & & \ddots & \\ & & & e_j^{\nu_j - 1} \end{bmatrix} \times E_{r/\nu_1 \nu_2 \cdots \nu_j},$$

$$b_j = E_{\nu_1 \nu_2 \dots \nu_{j-1}} \times \begin{bmatrix} 0 & \cdots & 0 & e \\ e & \cdots & 0 & 0 \\ \cdot & \cdots & \cdot & \cdot \\ \cdot & \cdots & \cdot & \cdot \\ 0 & \cdots & e & 0 \end{bmatrix} \times E_{r/\nu_1 \nu_2 \cdots \nu_j},$$

where ϵ_j belongs to K' and is a primitive root of the equation $x^{\nu_j} = e$, and e is the unit element of K'.

In order to go over to matrices of order n over D we have to replace in the matrices $a \in \mathrm{GL}(r, K')$, e and ϵ_j, respectively, by the matrices E_2 and $\begin{bmatrix} \cos \phi_j & -\sin \phi_j \\ \sin \phi_j & \cos \phi_j \end{bmatrix}$, where $\phi_j = 2\pi/\nu_j$.

Thus the group A is uniquely determined to within conjugacy in $\mathrm{GL}(n, D)$. The group Γ is contained in the normalizer N of A in $\mathrm{GL}(n, D)$. The index of A in N is finite. Therefore, the number of primitive soluble groups containing A as normal subgroup is finite.

Thus $\mathrm{GL}(n, D)$ has only a finite number of nonconjugate maximal primitive soluble subgroups. From this follows (see the proof of Theorem 20).

THEOREM 22. *The full linear group over the field of real numbers has only a finite number of nonconjugate maximal soluble subgroups.*

From the preceding arguments it follows that $\mathrm{GL}(n, D)$ for an odd n does not contain primitive soluble subgroups. Thus we have

THEOREM 23. *Every maximal irreducible soluble subgroup of the full linear group of odd degree n over the field of real numbers is conjugate to a group that* *is the semi-direct product of a maximal transitive soluble subgroup of S_n and the full diagonal group.*

EXAMPLE. Let p be a prime number. We shall construct all the maximal irreducible soluble subgroups of $GL(p, D)$. Two cases are possible: (1) $p>2$, (2) $p=2$. If (1) $p>2$, then by Theorem 23 a maximal soluble irreducible subgroup of $GL(p, D)$ is conjugate to the group $\Gamma=TH$, where T is the full metacyclic group of order $p(p-1)$ that permutes the basis vectors of the space $D^{(p)}$ and the normal subgroup H of Γ coincides with the diagonal subgroup of $GL(p, D)$; (2) $p=2$. (i) Γ is primitive. Γ has an abelian normal subgroup F consisting of all the matrices of the form $f=\begin{bmatrix} \alpha & -\beta \\ \beta & \alpha \end{bmatrix}$, $\alpha, \beta \in D$, $\alpha^2+\beta^2 \neq 0$. Now let $g \in \Gamma$; then

$$g^{-1}\begin{bmatrix} 0 & -1 \\ 1 & 0 \end{bmatrix} g = \pm \begin{bmatrix} 0 & -1 \\ 1 & 0 \end{bmatrix} \quad \text{or} \quad \begin{bmatrix} 0 & -1 \\ 1 & 0 \end{bmatrix} g = \pm g \begin{bmatrix} 0 & -1 \\ 1 & 0 \end{bmatrix}.$$

Hence,

$$g=\begin{bmatrix} 0 & 1 \\ 1 & 0 \end{bmatrix}^{\nu} f, \qquad \nu=0, 1, \quad f \in F.$$

(ii) Γ is imprimitive. Γ splits into two cosets:

$$H \text{ and } \begin{bmatrix} 0 & 1 \\ 1 & 0 \end{bmatrix} H,$$

where H is a diagonal subgroup of $GL(2, D)$.

CHAPTER III

NILPOTENT LINEAR GROUPS

In this chapter we shall study nilpotent subgroups of the full linear group $GL(n, P)$. We are mainly concerned with the case when the field P is algebraically closed. The following results will be obtained:

1. Let Γ be an irreducible nilpotent subgroup of $GL(n, P)$ of class l. If Z_1 is the center of Γ, then

$$\Gamma : Z_1 \leqq n\,!\, n^{(n-1)(l-1)}.$$[13]

2. If the characteristic of P is zero or prime to n, then $GL(n, P)$ has irreducible nilpotent subgroups of every class of nilpotency $l > 1$. But if the characteristic of P divides n, then $GL(n, P)$ does not have irreducible nilpotent subgroups.

3. The full linear group has only a finite number of irreducible nonconjugate maximal subgroups of a given class of nilpotency. Every irreducible nilpotent group of class l is contained in a maximal nilpotent group of the same class of nilpotency.[14]

4. The group $GL(n, P)$ has locally nilpotent irreducible subgroups if and only if the characteristic of P is zero or prime to n. All maximal locally nilpotent irreducible subgroups of $GL(n, P)$ are conjugate in $GL(n, P)$.

A similar statement holds for transitive nilpotent subgroups of the symmetric group S_n.

5. All maximal nilpotent transitive subgroups of the symmetric group S_n are conjugate in S_n.

The investigation of reducible nilpotent and locally nilpotent linear groups over an algebraically closed field completely reduces that of irreducible groups of smaller degrees.

In the book we give a description of all maximal locally nilpotent sub-

---

[13] This theorem is true for an arbitrary ground field. But in the statements 2-4 it is assumed that P is an algebraically closed field.

[14] We have in mind maximality among the groups of a given class of nilpotency. In the set of all irreducible nilpotent groups there are no maximal ones, because every irreducible nilpotent subgroup of $GL(n, P)$ of class l is contained in a nilpotent subgroup of a higher class of nilpotency.

groups (reducible and irreducible) of $\mathrm{GL}(n, P)$ in the case of an algebraically closed field P.

1. **Preliminary lemmas.** Let Γ be an irreducible nilpotent subgroup of $\mathrm{GL}(n, P)$ and Z_1 the center of Γ. If P is algebraically closed, then by Schur's lemma $Z_1 \subset PE_n$, i.e., in this case the center of Γ is isomorphic to a certain subgroup of the multiplicative group of P. But in the general case we have

LEMMA 18. *If Γ is an irreducible nilpotent subgroup of* $\mathrm{GL}(n, P)$ *and Z_1 the center of Γ, then Γ can be embedded in a linear group* $\mathrm{GL}(r, \Delta)$, *such that Z_1 becomes a subgroup of the multiplicative group of the field. Here Δ is an algebra over P and $n = r(\Delta : P)$.*

PROOF. The linear P-hull of Z_1 is a field Δ. In fact, Δ is a commutative algebra of finite rank over P. By Schur's lemma, Δ has no divisors of zero and is, therefore, a field. Since Z_1 is a normal subgroup of the irreducible group Γ, the space $P^{(n)}$ in which Γ acts can be represented in the form $P^{(n)} = Q_1 \dotplus \cdots \dotplus Q_r$, where Q_j are invariant subspaces, irreducible relative to Δ, of one and the same dimension m. Therefore, $Q_j = \Delta u_j$, $u_j \in Q_j$, and $P^{(n)}$ can be regarded as an r-dimensional space over Δ. Since each element of Γ is permutable with every element of Δ, $\Gamma \subset \mathrm{GL}(r, \Delta)$. The dimension of Q_j is equal to $\Delta : P$. Hence $n = r(\Delta : P)$. Obviously $Z_1 \subset \Delta$. The lemma is now proved.

If D is the multiplicative group of Δ, then $D\Gamma$ is also a nilpotent group whose center coincides with D. It is equally obvious that Γ and $D\Gamma$ are of one and the same class of nilpotency.

LEMMA 19. *Let Γ be an irreducible nilpotent subgroup of* $\mathrm{GL}(n, P)$, *$Z_0 = E \subset Z_1 \subset Z_2 \subset \cdots \subset Z_l = \Gamma$ the upper central series of Γ. Then the order of each element of the factor-group Z_2/Z_1 is a divisor of n.*

PROOF. If we can prove Lemma 19 for the case when $Z_1 \subset PE_n$, then it follows from Lemma 18 that it is true in the general case. Suppose then that $Z_1 \subset PE_n$. Now if $a \in Z_2$, $g \in \Gamma$, then $ag = \lambda ga$, $\lambda \in P$. Going over to the determinants $|a|$, $|g|$ of the matrices a and g we obtain $|a|\,|g| = \lambda^n |g|\,|a|$, $\lambda^n = 1$.

Therefore, $a^n g = \lambda^n g a^n = g a^n$, $a^n \in Z_1$. The lemma is now proved.

LEMMA 20. *If aZ_1 is an element of order k of Z_2/Z_1, then Γ contains an element g such that the order of the commutator $aga^{-1}g^{-1}$ is equal to k.*

PROOF. By Lemma 18 we may assume that $\Gamma \subset GL(r, \Delta)$, $Z_1 \subset \Delta$. Hence we obtain $(a,g) \in \Delta$, $(a,g)^r = 1$. On the other hand, as is easy to verify, $(a,g)(a,h) = (a,gh), g, h \in \Gamma$.

Therefore, all the commutators of the form (a,g) form a finite cyclic group whose order divides r. When the equation $(a^\alpha, g) = (a,g)^\alpha$ it follows that the order of this group is equal to k. This proves the lemma.

COROLLARY. *The order of an element of the factor-group Z_2/Z_1 cannot be divisible by the characteristic of P.*

LEMMA 21. *If the center Z_1 coincides with the multiplicative group of the field PE_n, then*

$$Z_2 : Z_1 = [Z_2] : P. \tag{1}$$

PROOF. Let $a_1, a_2, \cdots, a_t$ be representatives of arbitrary distinct cosets of Z_1 in Z_2. We shall show that $a_1, \cdots, a_t$ are linearly independent over P. For every $g \in \Gamma$ we have $g a_j g^{-1} = \gamma_j a_j$, where $\gamma_j \in P$; also for every pair $a_i, a_j, i \neq j$, we can find an element g in Γ such that $\gamma_i \neq \gamma_j$. Suppose now that $a_1, \cdots, a_t$ are linearly dependent. Among the nontrivial relations connecting $a_1, \cdots, a_t$ we take one that contains the smallest number of nonzero terms:

$$\lambda_1 a_1 + \lambda_2 a_2 + \cdots + \lambda_t a_t = 0. \tag{2}$$

We may assume that $\lambda_1 \neq 0$, $\lambda_2 \neq 0$. We choose a $g \in \Gamma$ such that $\lambda_1 \neq \lambda_2$. From (2) we obtain

$$\gamma_1(\lambda_1 a_1 + \lambda_2 a_2 + \cdots + \lambda_t a_t) - g(\lambda_1 a_1 + \lambda_2 a_2 + \cdots + \lambda_t a_t) g^{-1}$$
$$= \lambda_2(\gamma_1 - \gamma_2) a_2 + \cdots + \lambda_t(\gamma_1 - \gamma_t) a_t = 0.$$

The last relation contradicts the choice of (2) and the lemma is proved.

LEMMA 22. *Let k be the largest among the orders of elements of Z_2/Z_1. Then the orders of elements of the factor-groups Z_{j+1}/Z_j, $j = 1, \cdots, l-1$, are divisors of k.*

PROOF. For $j=1$ the lemma is trivial. Suppose that $j>1$ and that the lemma is already proved for Z_j/Z_{j-1}. For $g \in \Gamma$ and $a \in Z_{j+1}$ we can write $ga = bag$, where $b \in Z_j$. Hence,

$$gZ_{j-1} aZ_{j-1} = bZ_{j-1} aZ_{j-1} gZ_{j-1}.$$

Since $bZ_{j-1} gZ_{j-1} = gZ_{j-1} bZ_{j-1}$, we have

$$gZ_{j-1}(aZ_{j-1})^k = (bZ_{j-1})^k (aZ_{j-1})^k gZ_{j-1}.$$

By the induction hypothesis $(bZ_{j-1})^k = Z_{j-1}$. Hence, $(aZ_{j-1})^k \subset Z_j$, $(aZ_j)^k = Z_j$. The lemma is now proved.

COROLLARY. *The factor-group Γ/Z_1 is periodic, and the order of every element of Γ/Z_1 is a divisor of k^{l-1}.*

If P is an algebraically closed field, then the following theorem holds.

THEOREM 24. *Let Γ be an irreducible nilpotent subgroup of* $\mathrm{GL}(n, P)$. *Then $P^{(n)}$ has a basis $u_1, \cdots, u_n$ such that for every $g \in \Gamma$*

$$g(u_1) = \lambda_1 u_{i_1}, \cdots, g(u_n) = \lambda_n u_{i_n}, \qquad \lambda_j \in P, \tag{3}$$

where $i_1, \cdots, i_n$ is a permutation of the numbers $1, \cdots, n$. *In other words, Γ is conjugate with a monomial subgroup of* $\mathrm{GL}(n, P)$.

PROOF. The space $P^{(n)}$ can be represented in the form of a direct sum of subspaces $Q_1, Q_2, \cdots, Q_r$, $n \geqq r \geqq 1$, such that the elements of Γ permute the subspaces Q_j transitively and that the subgroup Γ_j of Γ consisting of all the elements of Γ that permute the vectors of Q_j within Q_j induces in Q_j a primitive group of degree n/r (see Chapter I, Lemma 2).

Now if Γ is nilpotent, then Γ is imprimitive for $n > r$. For suppose that $a \in Z_2 \setminus Z_1$. Then $(a)Z_1$ is an abelian normal subgroup of Γ and $(a)Z_1$ is not contained in PE_n. Therefore, Γ is imprimitive.

Since Γ_j induces in Q_j a nilpotent primitive group of degree n/r, we have $n/r = 1$, $n = r$. The theorem is now proved.

LEMMA 23. *Let Γ be an irreducible nilpotent subgroup of* $\mathrm{GL}(n, P)$, *where P is an algebraically closed field. Then Γ has an abelian normal subgroup $H \supset Z_1$,*[15] *such that Γ/H is isomorphic to a certain transitive nilpotent subgroup of the symmetric group S_n.*

PROOF. With an element g of Γ we associate the permutation

$$\begin{pmatrix} 1 \cdots n \\ i_1 \cdots i_n \end{pmatrix}$$

(see (3)). This correspondence is a homomorphic mapping of Γ into the

---

[15] Z_1 is the center of Γ.

symmetric group S_n. The kernel of the homomorphism is an abelian normal subgroup H. Therefore, Γ/H is isomorphic to a transitive nilpotent subgroup of S_n. This proves the lemma.

COROLLARY. *The factor-group of an irreducible nilpotent subgroup of* GL(n, P) *with respect to an arbitrary maximal abelian normal subgroup is isomorphic, in the case of an algebraically closed field P, to a transitive nilpotent subgroup of the symmetric group S_n.*

2. **Transitive nilpotent subgroups of the symmetric group.** Here we shall describe all the maximal transitive nilpotent subgroups of the symmetric group S_n and shall show that they are conjugate in S_n.

To begin with we mention that when p is a prime, a nilpotent transitive subgroup N of the symmetric group S_p is a cyclic group of order p. For the order of N is divisible by p, because N is transitive. Since N is nilpotent, the order of its center is also divisible by p.

Therefore, the center of the group contains a p-term cycle. Hence, it follows that every permutation of N is a power of this cycle.

LEMMA 24. *Let N be a transitive nilpotent subgroup of the symmetric group S_n. Then every prime divisor of the order of N is a divisor of n.*

PROOF. When n is a prime, the lemma is obvious. Suppose now that n is composite and that for all numbers less than n the lemma is proved. We shall prove it for n. The group N has intransitive normal subgroups (the cyclic subgroup formed by an element of prime order in the center is one of the intransitive normal subgroups of N). By a well-known theorem, N is imprimitive. Suppose that the n symbols permuted by N split into s systems of imprimitivity, s/n, $1<s<n$. It is clear that N can be mapped homomorphically onto a transitive group of permutations $\bar{N}$ of degree s. The kernel N_0 of this homomorphism consists of all elements of N that permute the symbols within the systems of imprimitivity. This kernel N_0 is contained in the direct product of s transitive nilpotent groups of degree n/s. By the induction hypothesis, the prime divisors of the order of $\bar{N}$ occur in s, and the prime divisors of the order of N_0 occur in N/s. Hence, the lemma follows.

Thus n and the order of N have the same prime divisors. A nilpotent subgroup of the symmetric group S_n is called maximal if it is not contained in another nilpotent subgroup of S_n.

LEMMA 25. *The maximal nilpotent subgroups of S_{p^ν}, where p is a prime* *number, and conjugate in S_{p^ν}, because they are all Sylow p-subgroups of the symmetric group S_{p^ν}.*

PROOF. By Lemma 24, every transitive nilpotent subgroup of S_{p^ν} is a p-group. Therefore, Lemma 25 follows from Sylow's Second Theorem.

In what follows we shall denote one of the Sylow p-subgroups of the symmetric group S_{p^ν} by N_{p^ν}. *Now let*

$$n = p_1^{\nu 1} p_2^{\nu 2} \cdots p_k^{\nu k} \tag{i}$$

where p_j are distinct prime numbers. We shall construct one transitive nilpotent subgroup of S_n, isomorphic to the direct product of the k groups $N_{p_1^{\nu 1}}, \cdots, N_{p_k^{\nu k}}$. Let ξ range over the n symbols permuted by S_n.

We write ξ in the form $\xi = [\xi_1, \cdots, \xi_j, \cdots, \xi_k]$, where ξ_j ranges over $p_j^{\nu j}$ symbols. Now if ϕ_j ranges over all the permutations of $N_{pj}^{\nu j}$, then all f_j, where $f_j(\xi) = f_j[\xi_1, \cdots, \xi_j, \cdots, \xi_k] = [\xi_1, \cdots, \phi_j(\xi_j), \cdots, \xi_k]$ form a group $N^{(j)}$ isomorphic to $N_{p_j^{\nu j}}$. We set

$$N_n = N^{(1)} \cdots N^{(k)}. \tag{ii}$$

Obviously, the product (ii) is direct, N_n is nilpotent and transitive. It could be shown immediately that N_n is a maximal nilpotent subgroup of S_n, but we shall show below that every transitive nilpotent subgroup of S_n is conjugate in S_n to a certain subgroup of N_n, and in this way we shall establish the maximality of N_n, the conjugacy of all maximal nilpotent transitive subgroups of S_n, and we shall obtain a description of them.

Let N be transitive nilpotent subgroup of S_n, where $n = p_1^{\nu 1} \cdots p_k^{\nu k}$, $k > 1$. By Lemma 24, the order N is of the form

$$p_1^{\alpha 1} \cdots p_k^{\alpha k}, \quad \alpha_j \geqq \nu_j. \tag{iii}$$

We write N in the form of a direct product HF, where H is of order $p_1^{\alpha 1}$ and F of order $p_2^{\alpha 2} \cdots p_k^{\alpha k}$.

LEMMA 26. *The symbols permuted by N can be enumerated by number pairs $[x, y]$, such that for $h \in H$ and $f \in F$*

$$h[x, y] = [\psi(x), y], \quad f[x, y] = [x, \phi(y)],$$

where x ranges over $p_1^{\nu 1}$ symbols and y over $p_2^{\nu 2} \cdots p_k^{\nu k}$ symbols, $\psi(x)$ permutes the symbols x transitively, and $\phi(y)$ permutes the symbols y transitively.

PROOF. Since the order of F is not divisible by n, F is intransitive. The systems of transitivity of F are systems of imprimitivity of N. Let s be the number of these systems and r the number of symbols in each system. Since F is contained in the direct product of s nilpotent groups of degree r, the order of F and the number r have the same prime divisors: $p_2,\cdots,p_k$. Since N is transitive and F leaves every system of imprimitivity invariant, H permutes these systems transitively. Hence, it follows that s is a divisor of the order of H, i.e., $s=p_1^{\beta_1}$ and $r=p_2^{\beta_2}\cdots p_k^{\beta_k}$. But $rs=n$, hence, $s=p_1^{\nu_1}$, $r=p_2^{\nu_2}\cdots p_k^{\nu_k}$.

Let us now show that the symbols permuted by N can be so enumerated that every permutation f of F induces in all systems of imprimitivity one and the same permutation of degree r. Let $1,2,\cdots,r$ be the symbols of one system of imprimitivity. Then the symbols of every system of imprimitivity can be written in the form $x_1,x_2,\cdots,x_r$, where $x_j=h_x(j)$, $h_x\in H$.

Let $f(j)=i_j$; then $f(x_j)=fh_x(j)=h_xf(j)=x_{i_j}$. Therefore, if instead of x_1, $x_2,\cdots,x_r$ we write $[x,1]$, $[x,2],\cdots,[x,r]$, then $f[x,y]=[x,\phi(y)]$, $x=1,\cdots,s$, $y=1,\cdots,r$. Now let us find the form of $h[x,y]$. In H there are s permutations h_x, $x=1,\cdots,s$, such that $h_x[1,y]=[x,y]$. We shall show that for every $h\in H$ we have $h[1,y]=[x,y]$. Let $h[1,y]=[x,y_1]$ and $y_1\neq y$. Then $h_x^{-1}h[1,y]=[1,y_1]$. $h_x^{-1}h$ induces in the system $[1,1]$, $[1,2]$, $\cdots$, $[1,r]$ a certain permutation h_0. Now if F_0 is the group that F induces in the same system, then, obviously, h_0 is permutable with every permutation of F_0. Thus $(h_0)F_0$ is a nilpotent transitive group of degree $r=p_2^{\nu_2}\cdots p_k^{\nu_k}$. By Lemma 24, the order of $(h_0)F_0$ is equal to $p_2^{\gamma_2}\cdots p_k^{\gamma_k}$.

On the other hand, $h_0\neq e$ is an element of a homomorphic image of a certain subgroup of H. Therefore, the order of h_0 is $p_1^{\gamma_1}$. This contradiction proves the formula $h[1,y]=[x,y]$. Hence, it follows easily that

$$h[x,y]=[\psi(x),y].$$

The lemma is now proved.

THEOREM 25. *Every nilpotent transitive subgroup N of the symmetric group S_n is conjugate to a certain subgroup of N_n.*

PROOF. Let $n=p_1^{\nu_1}\cdots p_k^{\nu_k}$. For $k=1$ the theorem is proved. Suppose that $k>1$ and that the theorem is proved for $k-1$. $N=HF$. By the induction hypothesis, F is conjugate to a certain subgroup of the group $N_{n/p_1^{\nu_1}}=N^{(2)}N^{(3)}\cdots N^{(k)}$ (see (ii)). Therefore, $N=HF$ is conjugate to a certain subgroup of N_n. This proves the theorem.

From Theorem 25 we deduce

THEOREM 26. *All transitive maximal nilpotent subgroups of a symmetric group are conjugate to one another. Furthermore, if* $n = p_1^{\nu_1} \cdots p_k^{\nu_k}$, *then a transitive maximal nilpotent subgroup of the symmetric group* S_n *is isomorphic to the direct product of Sylow* p_j*-subgroups of the symmetric groups* $S_{p_1^{\nu_1}}, \cdots, S_{p_k^{\nu_k}}$.

It is easy to compute that the order of a maximal transitive nilpotent subgroup of S_n is equal to

$$p_1^{\mu_1} p_2^{\mu_2} \cdots p_k^{\mu_k},$$

where

$$\mu_j = \frac{p_j^{\nu_j} - 1}{p_j - 1}.$$

The Sylow p-subgroups N_{p^ν} of the symmetric group S_{p^ν} have been investigated by L. Kalužnin (see, for example, [**35**]).

3. **The theorem on the index of the center. Corollaries.**

THEOREM 27. *Let* Γ *be an irreducible nilpotent subgroup of* GL(n, P) *of class* l *and* Z_1 *the center of* Γ. *Then*

$$\Gamma : Z_1 \leq n!\, n^{(n-1)(l-1)} = \nu(n, l).$$

PROOF. To begin with, we shall assume that P is algebraically closed and that Z_1 coincides with the multiplicative group of the field PE_n. By Theorem 24, Γ has an abelian normal subgroup $H \supset Z_1$ whose index does not exceed $n!$. The matrices $h \in H$ can be reduced to the diagonal form

$$h = \begin{bmatrix} \lambda_1 & & & & \\ & \lambda_2 & & & \\ & & \cdot & & \\ & & & \cdot & \\ & & & & \lambda_n \end{bmatrix}.$$

By Lemma 22, $h^{k^{l-1}} \in Z_1$, therefore, $\lambda_1^{k^{l-1}} = \lambda_2^{k^{l-1}} = \cdots = \lambda_n^{k^{l-1}}$. Hence,

$$h = \lambda_1 \begin{bmatrix} 1 & & & & \\ & \eta_2 & & & \\ & & \cdot & & \\ & & & \cdot & \\ & & & & \eta_n \end{bmatrix}, \qquad \text{where } \eta_j^{k^{l-1}} = 1.$$

Therefore, the number of cosets of Z_1 in H does not exceed

$$(k^{l-1})^{n-1} \leqq n^{(n-1)(l-1)}.$$

Hence, $\Gamma : Z_1 \leqq n\,!\, n^{(n-1)(l-1)}$.

Now we proceed to the general case. Let P be an arbitrary field. We examine the linear P-hull $[\Gamma]$ of Γ. The algebra $[\Gamma]$ is a simple algebra over P. Let Δ be the center of $[\Gamma]$; then $[\Gamma] : \Delta = r^2$, $r \leqq n$. We shall regard $[\Gamma]$ as an algebra over Δ.

Now if Ω is an algebraically closed field containing Δ, then by extending the ground field Δ of the algebra $[\Gamma]$ to Ω we obtain $[\Gamma] \times \Omega$, a simple central algebra over Ω. Therefore, $[\Gamma] \times \Omega \cong \Omega_r$, Ω_r is the full matrix ring over Ω. $[\Gamma] \times \Omega$ contains r^2 linearly independent elements of the group Γ.

Consequently, Ω_r contains an irreducible group Γ' isomorphic to Γ. The product $G = \Gamma' M$, where M is the multiplicative group of the field Ω, is an irreducible nilpotent subgroup of $\mathrm{GL}(r, \Omega)$ of class l. The center of G coincides with M.

By what has been shown, $G : M \leqq r\,!\, r^{(r-1)(l-1)}$. Since $\Gamma' : Z_1' \leqq G : M$, we have

$$\Gamma : Z_1 \leqq r\,!\, r^{(r-1)(l-1)} \leqq n\,!\, n^{(n-1)(l-1)} = \nu(n, l).$$

The theorem is now proved.

THEOREM 28. *Let Γ be an irreducible nilpotent subgroup of* $\mathrm{GL}(n, P)$, *where P is algebraically closed. Then the number n and the order of the factor-group Γ / Z_1 have the same prime divisors.*

PROOF. By Lemmas 22 and 19, every prime divisor of $\Gamma : Z_1$ divides n. On the other hand, $\Gamma : Z_1 = (\Gamma : H)(H : Z_1)$. $\Gamma : H$ is the order of a certain transitive nilpotent subgroup of S_n.[16] Therefore, $\Gamma : Z_1$ is divisible by n. This proves the theorem.

COROLLARY 1. *The numbers k and n (see Lemma 22) have the same prime divisors.*

COROLLARY 2. *If the characteristic of the algebraically closed field P is a prime divisor of n, then* $\mathrm{GL}(n, P)$ *has no irreducible nilpotent subgroups (see the corollary to Lemma 20).*

[16] See Lemma 23.

LEMMA 27. *If the center of an irreducible nilpotent subgroup* Γ *of* $\mathrm{GL}(n,P)$ *is contained in* PE_n, *then the intersection of* Γ *with the special linear group* $\mathrm{SL}(n,P)$ *is a finite group whose order does not exceed* $n\nu(n,l)$ *(see Theorem 27).*

PROOF. We have that $\Gamma : Z_1 \leqq \nu(n, l)$. If $\Gamma_0 = \Gamma \cap \mathrm{SL}(n,P)$, then $\Gamma_0 : (Z_1 \cap \Gamma_0) \leqq \nu(n, l)$, because $\Gamma_0 Z_1/Z_1 \cong \Gamma_0/Z_1 \cap \Gamma_0$. $Z_1 \cap \Gamma_0 = Z_1 \cap \mathrm{SL}(n,P)$. For $c \in Z_1 \cap \mathrm{SL}(n,P)$ we can write $c = \lambda E_n$, $\lambda^n = 1$. Therefore, the order of $Z_1 \cap \Gamma_0$ is not greater than n. The lemma is proved.

THEOREM 29. *Let* Γ *be an irreducible nilpotent subgroup of* $\mathrm{GL}(n,P)$, *where* P *is an algebraically closed field. Then the group* $\Gamma_0 = \Gamma \cap \mathrm{SL}(n,P)$ *is finite, and the order of* Γ_0 *and* n *have the same prime divisors. If the center* Z_1 *of* Γ *consist of all nonsingular matrices* PE_n, *then* $\Gamma = \Gamma_0 Z_1$.

PROOF. The finiteness of $\Gamma_0 = \Gamma \cap \mathrm{SL}(n,P)$ follows from Lemma 27. We have to show that the order of Γ_0 and n have the same set of prime divisors. Suppose first of all that the center of Γ coincides with the multiplicative group M of the field PE_n. For every $g \in \Gamma$ we can find a $\lambda \in P$ such that $\lambda^{-1} g \in \Gamma_0$. Therefore, $\Gamma = \Gamma_0 M = \Gamma_0 Z_1$. Furthermore, $\Gamma/Z_1 = \Gamma_0 M/M \cong \Gamma_0/M \cap \Gamma_0 = \Gamma_0/M \cap \mathrm{SL}(n,P)$. Therefore, $n(\Gamma : M) = \Gamma_0 : E$.

By Theorem 28, $\Gamma : Z_1$ and n have the same prime divisors. Thus, for the case $Z_1 = M$ the theorem is proved. Now suppose that $Z_1 \subset M$. We set $\Gamma' = \Gamma M$, $\Gamma_0' = \Gamma' \cap \mathrm{SL}(n,P)$. Then $n(\Gamma : M) = \Gamma_0' : E$. It is easy to figure out that $\Gamma_0' : E = d(\Gamma_0 : E)$, where d/n, $\Gamma_0 = \Gamma \cap \mathrm{SL}(n,P)$. Consequently, $\Gamma_0 : E$ and n have the same prime divisors. The proof of the theorem is now complete.

If Γ is a nilpotent subgroup of $\mathrm{GL}(n,P)$ of class l and is not contained in another nilpotent subgroup of $\mathrm{GL}(n,P)$ of the same class, then Γ is called a maximal nilpotent subgroup of $\mathrm{GL}(n,P)$ of class l.

THEOREM 30. *If* P *is algebraically closed, then among the irreducible maximal nilpotent subgroups of* $\mathrm{GL}(n,P)$ *of a given class* l, *only a finite number are nonconjugate in* $\mathrm{GL}(n,P)$.

PROOF. Obviously, the center of a maximal nilpotent irreducible subgroup Γ of $\mathrm{GL}(n,P)$ of a given class l is equal to the multiplicative group of the field PE_n. Therefore, $\Gamma = \Gamma_0 Z_1$, where Γ_0 is a group whose order does not exceed the number $n\nu(n, l)$. The number of nonisomorphic groups whose orders are not greater than $n\nu(n, l)$ is finite. A finite group can only have a finite number of inequivalent representations in GL(n, P). Hence, the theorem follows.

THEOREM 31. *Let G be a finite nilpotent subgroup of* GL(n, P) *of class l. If the characteristic of P is equal to zero or prime to the order of G, then the index of the center Z of G does not exceed the number* $\nu(n, l) = n!\, n^{(n-1)(l-1)}$

PROOF. The group G is a completely reducible subgroup of GL(n, P). If $n_1, \cdots, n_t$ are the degrees of the irreducible blocks of G, then we have by Theorem 27: $G:Z \leqq n_1!\, n_1^{(n_1-1)(l-1)} \cdots n_t!\, n_t^{(n_t-1)(l-1)} \leqq n!\, n^{(n-1)(l-1)}$. This proves the theorem.

4. **Metabelian irreducible subgroups of** GL(n, P). Nilpotent groups of class 2 are also called metabelian groups.[17]

THEOREM 32. *Let Γ be a nilpotent irreducible subgroup of* GL(n, P), *where P is an algebraically closed field. If the second hypercenter Z_2 of Γ is irreducible, then Γ is metabelian, i.e., $\Gamma = Z_2$.*

PROOF. We write the finite abelian group Z_2/Z_1 in the form of a direct product of ρ cyclic groups of the orders $l_1, l_2, \cdots, l_\rho$;

$$Z_2/Z_1 = (c_1Z_1)(c_2Z_1)\cdots(c_\rho Z_1);\ Z_2 = (c_1)(c_2)\cdots(c_\rho)Z_1$$

$$Z_2 : Z_1 = l_1, l_2, \cdots, l_\rho.$$

Since $c_j Z_1$ is of order l_j, by Lemma 20 Γ contains an element g_j such that $(c_j, g_j) = \eta_j E_n$, where η_j is a primitive root of the equation $x^{l_j} = 1$, $\eta_j \in P$. For every $g \in \Gamma$ we have $(c_j, g) = \eta_j^{\alpha} E_n$. Therefore, $\Gamma = (g_j) F_j$, where F is the centralizer of c_j in Γ. It is easy to see that $\Gamma : F_j = l_j$. Now if F is the centralizer of Z_2 in Γ, then $\Gamma : F \leqq l_1 l_2 \cdots l_\rho$, because F is the intersection of the groups F_j. Since Z_2 is irreducible, we have $F = Z_1$. Therefore, $\Gamma : Z_1 \leqq l_1 l_2 \cdots l_\rho = Z_2 : Z_1$. Hence, $\Gamma = Z_2$.

THEOREM 33. *Every irreducible metabelian subgroup of* GL(n, P) *(P is algebraically closed) whose center coincides with the multiplicative group M of the field PE_n is a maximal metabelian subgroup of* GL(n, P).

[17] Translator's note. The term metabelian is usually applied to groups with an abelian derived group without the assumption that it is contained in the center.

PROOF. Suppose that Γ is an irreducible metabelian subgroup of $GL(n, P)$ and that the center of Γ is equal to M. By Lemma 21 we have: $\Gamma : M = Z_2 : M = [Z_2] : P = n^2$. But if $G \supseteq \Gamma$ and is also metabelian, then $G : M = n^2$. Hence $G = \Gamma$. The theorem is proved.

We shall now give a description of all maximal irreducible metabelian subgroups of $GL(n, P)$, assuming that P is algebraically closed.

If the Characteristic of P is a prime divisor of n, then by Theorem 28[18] there are no nilpotent irreducible subgroups in $GL(n, P)$. We shall now assume that the characteristic of P is zero or prime to n.

THEOREM 34. *Suppose that n is written in the form*

$$n = k_1 k_2 \cdots k_t, \qquad k_j / k_i, \;\; j > i, \;\; k_t > 1. \tag{4}$$

Then:

1. $GL(n, P)$ *contains a maximal irreducible metabelian subgroup* $\Gamma^2_{k_1 k_2 \cdots k_t}$ *whose matrices g can be represented in the form:*

$$g = \lambda a_1^{\alpha_1} b_1^{\beta_1} \cdots a_t^{\alpha_t} b_t^{\beta_t}, \qquad \lambda \in P \tag{5}$$

$$a_j = E_{k_1 \cdots k_{j-1}} \times \begin{bmatrix} 1 & & & \\ & \epsilon_j & & \\ & & \ddots & \\ & & & \epsilon_j^{k_j - 1} \end{bmatrix} \times E_{n/(k_1 \cdots k_j)},$$

$$b_j = E_{k_1 \cdots k_{j-1}} \times \begin{bmatrix} 0 & 0 & \cdots & 0 & 1 \\ 1 & 0 & \cdots & 0 & 0 \\ 0 & 1 & \cdots & 0 & 0 \\ \vdots & \vdots & \cdots & \vdots & \vdots \\ 0 & 0 & \cdots & 1 & 0 \end{bmatrix} \times E_{n/(k_1 \cdots k_j)}, \qquad 0 \leqq \alpha_j, \quad \beta_j \leqq k_j \tag{6}$$

ϵ_j is a primitive root of $x^{k_j} = 1$, $\epsilon_j \in P$.

2. *Distinct decompositions of n of the form* (4) *determine nonisomorphic groups* $\Gamma^2_{k_1 k_2 \cdots k_t}$.

3. *Every maximal irreducible metabelian subgroup of* $GL(n, P)$ *is conjugate in* $GL(n, P)$ *to* $\Gamma^2_{k_1 k_2 \cdots k_t}$ *determined by a certain decomposition of n of the form* (4).

---

[18] See Corollary 2.

PROOF. It is easy to verify that $(a_j, b_j)=\epsilon_j E_n$, $(a_i, b_j)=(a_i, a_j)=(b_i, b_j)=E_n$, $j\neq i$, and $a_j^{k_j}=b_j^{k_j}=E_n$. Hence, it follows that the group $\Gamma^2_{k_1k_2\cdots k_t}$ is metabelian. From this there follow the relations:

$$(a_j, a_1^{\alpha_1}b_1^{\beta_1}\cdots a_t^{\alpha_t}b_t^{\beta_t})=\epsilon_j^{\beta_j}E_n,$$

$$(b_j, a_1^{\alpha_1}b_1^{\beta_1}\cdots a_t^{\alpha_t}b_t^{\beta_t})=\epsilon_j^{-\alpha_j}E_n.$$

Hence, for any two elements c and d of the form

$$a_1^{\alpha_1}b_1^{\beta_1}\cdots a_t^{\alpha_t}b_t^{\beta_t} \qquad 0\leqq \alpha_j, \beta_j<k_j \tag{7}$$

with distinct systems of exponents we can find in $\Gamma^2_{k_1k_2\cdots k_t}$ an element g such that $(g, c)\neq(g, d)$. Hence, as is clear from the proof of Lemma 21, there follows the linear independence of the elements of the form (7). Since the number of the elements of the form (7) is equal to $k_1^2k_2^2\cdots k_t^2=n^2$, therefore, $\Gamma^2_{k_1k_2\cdots k_t}$ is irreducible. By Theorem 33, $\Gamma^2_{k_1k_2\cdots k_t}$ is maximal. The first statement of Theorem 34 is now proved.

$\Gamma^2_{k_1k_2\cdots k_t}/Z_1$ can be represented as a direct product of $2t$ cyclic groups:

$$(a_1Z_1)(b_1Z_1)\cdots(a_tZ_1)(b_tZ_1)$$

of order $k_1, k_1, \cdots, k_t, k_t$. Therefore, to distinct decompositions of n of the form (4) there correspond nonisomorphic groups $\Gamma^2_{k_1k_2\cdots k_t}$.

Now we have to show that every maximal irreducible metabelian subgroup Γ of $\mathrm{GL}(n, P)$ is conjugate to one of the groups of the form $\Gamma^2_{k_1k_2\cdots k_t}$. As in the proof in Theorem 3 we can establish the existence in Γ of elements $c_1, d_1, \cdots, c_t, d_t$ such that $g\in\Gamma$ is representable in the form

$$g=\lambda c_1^{\alpha_1}d_1^{\beta_1}\cdots c_t^{\alpha_t}d_t^{\beta_t}, \qquad \lambda\in P$$

$$(c_j, d_j)=\epsilon_jE_n, \qquad (c_i, c_j)=(c_i, d_j)=(d_i, d_j)=E_n, \qquad i\neq j$$

ϵ_j is a primitive root of the equation $x_j^{k_j}=1$, $\epsilon_j\in P$,

$$0\leqq\alpha_j, \beta_j<k_j,\ k_1k_2\cdots k_t=n,\ \ k_{j+1}/k_j,\ \ j=1, \cdots, t-1.$$

Obviously, $c_j^{k_j}, d_j^{k_j}\in PE_n$. Since P is algebraically closed, we may assume that $c_j^{k_j}=d_j^{k_j}=E_n$. Therefore, Γ is isomorphic to $\Gamma^2_{k_1k_2\cdots k_t}$, and the isomorphism $\lambda c_1^{\alpha_1}d_1^{\beta_1}\cdots c_t^{\alpha_t}d_t^{\beta_t}\to\lambda a_1^{\alpha_1}b_1^{\beta_1}\cdots a_t^{\alpha_t}b_t^{\beta_t}$ can be extended to an automorphism

$$\sum\lambda_{\alpha_1,\ldots,\beta_t}c_1^{\alpha_1}d_1^{\beta_1}\cdots c_t^{\alpha_t}b_t^{\beta_t}\to\sum\lambda_{\alpha_1,\ldots,\beta_t}a_1^{\alpha_1}b_1^{\beta_1}\cdots a_t^{\alpha_t}b_t^{\beta_t}$$

of the algebra $P_n=[\Gamma]=[\Gamma^2_{k_1k_2\cdots k_t}]$.

This implies the conjugacy of Γ and $\Gamma^2_{k_1k_2\cdots k_t}$ in $\mathrm{GL}(n, P)$. The proof of the theorem is now complete.

COROLLARY. *Two maximal irreducible metabelian subgroups of* GL(n, P) *are conjugate in* GL(n, P) *if their factor-groups with respect to the center are isomorphic.*

5. One chain of nilpotent irreducible subgroups of GL(n, P).

LEMMA 28. *Suppose that*

$$h=\begin{bmatrix} 0 & 0 & \cdots & 0 & 1 \\ 1 & 0 & \cdots & 0 & 0 \\ 0 & 1 & \cdots & 0 & 0 \\ \cdot & \cdot & \cdots & \cdot & \cdot \\ \cdot & \cdot & \cdots & \cdot & \cdot \\ 0 & 0 & \cdots & 1 & 0 \end{bmatrix} \qquad (\text{of order } n)$$

and that b is an arbitrary diagonal matrix whose determinant is equal to 1. *Then we can find a diagonal matrix c such that*

$$(c, h) = chc^{-1}h^{-1} = b \tag{8}$$

If c, d are diagonal matrices and $(c, h) = (d, h)$, then

$$d = \lambda c, \qquad \lambda \in P.$$

PROOF. We set

$$b=\begin{bmatrix} \beta_0 & & & & \\ & \beta_1 & & & \\ & & \cdot & & \\ & & & \cdot & \\ & & & & \beta_{n-1} \end{bmatrix}.$$

Then, as is easy to verify, the matrix

$$c=\begin{bmatrix} 1 & & & & \\ & \gamma_1 & & & \\ & & \cdot & & \\ & & & \cdot & \\ & & & & \gamma_{n-1} \end{bmatrix}, \qquad \text{where } \gamma_j = \beta_1\beta_2\cdots\beta_j, \ j = 1, \cdots, n-1$$

satisfies condition (8).

Now if c and d are diagonal matrices and $(c, h) = (d, h)$, then $(c^{-1}d, h) = E_n$. Hence, $c^{-1}d = \lambda E_n$, $d = \lambda c$. This proves the lemma.

Now let P be an algebraically closed field whose characteristic is zero or prime to n. Using Lemma 28, we construct an increasing chain of irreducible nilpotent subgroups of GL(n, P) containing a group of every class of nilpotency.

We begin by constructing an auxiliary chain of abelian subgroups of GL(n, P):

$$Z_1, Z_2=(c_2)Z_1, Z_3, \cdots, Z_j, \cdots, \tag{9}$$

where Z_1 is the multiplicative group of PE_n,

$$c_2=\begin{bmatrix} 1 & & & & \\ & \epsilon & & & \\ & & \cdot & & \\ & & & \cdot & \\ & & & & \epsilon^{n-1} \end{bmatrix},$$

ϵ is a primitive root of the equation $x^n=1$, $\epsilon \in P$, Z_j is the set of all diagonal matrices d of GL(n, P) satisfying the condition $(d, h) \in Z_{j-1}$, $j=2, 3, \cdots$,

$$h=\begin{bmatrix} 0 & 0 & \cdots & 0 & 1 \\ 1 & 0 & \cdots & 0 & 0 \\ 0 & 1 & \cdots & 0 & 0 \\ \cdot & \cdot & \cdots & \cdot & \cdot \\ \cdot & \cdot & \cdots & \cdot & \cdot \\ 0 & 0 & \cdots & 1 & 0 \end{bmatrix}.$$

LEMMA 29. *Z_{j+1}/Z_j is a cyclic group of order n for every $j \geqq 1$.*

PROOF. For $j=1$ the lemma is obvious. Suppose that it has been proved that Z_j/Z_{j-1} is a cyclic group of order n. We shall show this for Z_{j+1}/Z_j. By the induction hypothesis $Z_j=(c_j)Z_{j-1}$, $1, c_j, \cdots, c_j^{n-1}$ is a complete system of coset representatives of Z_{j-1} in Z_j. Now we shall show that two matrices c and d of Z_{j+1} lie in one coset of Z_j if and only if the matrices (c, h) and (d, h) belong to one and the same coset of Z_{j-1}. Suppose that

$$chc^{-1}h^{-1}=d_{j-1}dhd^{-1}h^{-1}, \qquad \text{where} \qquad d_{j-1} \in Z_{j-1}.$$

Then

$$d^{-1}ch=d_{j-1}hd^{-1}c, \qquad (d^{-1}c, h)=d_{j-1} \in Z_{j-1}.$$

Therefore, $d^{-1}c \in Z_j$, $c \in dZ_j$. Conversely, let $c=d_j d$, where $d_j \in Z_j$. $(c, h)=(d_j d, h)=(d_j, h)$ and $(d, h)=d_{j-1}(d, h)$. Therefore, (c, h) and (d, h) lie in one coset of Z_{j-1}.

By Lemma 28 we can find in Z_{j+1} a matrix c_{j+1} such that $(c_{j+1}, h)=\lambda c_j$, where $|\lambda c_j|=1$. Further, $(c_{j+1}^\alpha, h)=(c_{j+1}, h)^\alpha=\lambda^\alpha c_j^\alpha$.

In virtue of the arguments just given $1, c_{j+1}, \cdots, c_{j+1}^{n-1}$ is a complete system of coset representatives of Z_j in Z_{j+1}. The lemma is proved.

Now we introduce groups Γ_n^l, setting $\Gamma_n^l=(h)Z_l$, $l\geqq 2$.

LEMMA 30. *Γ_n^l is an irreducible nilpotent group of class l. The group Z_j of (9) is the jth hypercenter of Γ_n^l for $j<l$.*

PROOF. The group Γ_n^l is irreducible, because Γ_n^l has the n^2 linearly independent matrices $c_2^\alpha h^\beta$, $0\leqq\alpha$, $\beta<n$. Obviously, the center of Γ_n^l coincides with Z_1. Suppose that it is already proved that the $(j-1)$th hypercenter of Γ_n^l is equal to the group Z_{j-1} in (9). Then we shall show that the jth hypercenter of Γ_n^l coincides with Z_j, provided $j<l$. Obviously, $(Z_j,\ \Gamma_n^l)=(Z_j,\ (h)Z_l)=(Z_j,\ (h))\in Z_{j-1}$.

Therefore, Z_j is contained in the jth hypercenter of Γ_n^l. Moreover, every diagonal matrix of the jth hypercenter lies in Z_j. But if $d\in\Gamma_n^l$ and is not diagonal, then $d=h^\alpha c$, $0<\alpha<n$, $c\in Z_l$. $(c_l,\ d)=(c_l,\ h^\alpha c)=(c_l,\ h^\alpha)=\lambda c_{l-1}^\alpha$ is not contained in Z_{j-1}. Thus, d cannot lie in the jth hypercenter of Γ_n^l. Therefore, Z_j is the jth hypercenter of Γ_n^l. Obviously, $\Gamma_n^l:Z_{l-1}=n^2$, $\Gamma_n^l=(h)(c_{l-1})Z_{l-1}$, Γ_n^l/Z_{l-1} is the direct product of two copies of a cyclic group of order n, Γ_n^l is nilpotent of class l. $\Gamma_n^l:Z_1=n^l$.

LEMMA 31. *Γ_n^l is maximal among the nilpotent subgroups of* GL(n,P) *of class l.*

PROOF. Suppose that $\Gamma_n^l\subseteq G$, where G is a nilpotent subgroup of GL(n,P) of class l. Let $E=G_0\subset G_1\subset\cdots\subset G_{l-1}\subset G$ be the upper central series of G. Obviously, $G_1=Z_1$. Suppose that $G_i\subseteq Z_i$ for $i<j$. We shall then show that $G_j\subseteq Z_j$ for $j<l$. If $g_j\in G_j$, then $(g_j,\ h)=d_{j-1}\in G_{j-1}\subseteq Z_{j-1}$, $|d_{j-1}|=1$. Therefore, Z_j contains an element d_j such that $(d_j,\ h)=(g_j,\ h)=d_{j-1}$. Hence, $g_j=d_j v$, where $(v,\ h)=E_n$. Let us examine $(c_2,\ g_j)$. $(c_2,\ g_j)=(c_2,\ d_j v)=d'_{j-1}\in G_{j-1}\subseteq Z_{j-1}$, i.e., $c_2 d_j v c_2^{-1}v^{-1}d_j^{-1}$ is a diagonal matrix. Therefore, $(c_2, g_j)=(c_2,\ v)$. Furthermore, $(h,\ d'_{j-1})=(h,\ (c_2,\ v))=hc_2vc_2^{-1}v^{-1}h^{-1}vc_2v^{-1}c_2^{-1}=E_n$. Therefore, $(c_2 v)=\epsilon^\alpha E_n$, $v=\lambda h^\alpha$, $g_j=\lambda d_j h^\alpha$. $(c_{j+1}, g_j)=(c_{j+1}, \lambda d_j h^\alpha)=(c_{j+1}, h^\alpha)=\rho c_j^\alpha\in Z_{j-1}$. Consequently, $\alpha=0$, $g_j=\lambda d_j\in Z_j$. Thus, $G_j\subseteq Z_j$, $j<l$. In particular, $G_{l-1}\subseteq Z_{l-1}$. Now if $g\in G$, then $(g,\ h)=d_{l-1}\in G_{l-1}\subseteq Z_{l-1}$, $|d_{l-1}|=1$. Therefore, there is a $d_l\in Z_l$ such that $(d_l,\ h)=d_{l-1}$. $g=d_l v$, $(v,\ h)=E_n$, $v=\lambda h^\alpha$, $g\in\Gamma_n^l=(h)Z_l$. The lemma is now proved.

From the last three lemmas we derive

THEOREM 35. *If the characteristic of P is zero or prime to n, then* GL(n,P) *has a countable chain of nilpotent irreducible subgroups*

$$\Gamma_n^2\subset\Gamma_n^3\subset\cdots\subset\Gamma_n^l\subset\cdots. \tag{10}$$

The group Γ_n^l of class l is not contained in another nilpotent subgroup of $\mathrm{GL}(n, P)$ of the same class. The factors Z_{j+1}/Z_j of the upper central series of Γ_n^l for $1 \leqq j < l-1$ are cyclic groups of order n. Γ_n^l/Z_{l-1} is the direct product of two cyclic groups of order n. $\Gamma_n^l : Z_1 = n^l$.

COROLLARY. *For every preassigned $l > 1$, $\mathrm{GL}(n, P)$ contains a finite nilpotent irreducible subgroup Γ_0 of class l and of order n^{l+1}.*

In fact, we can take for Γ_0 the intersection $\Gamma_n^l \cap \mathrm{SL}(n, P)$, where $\mathrm{SL}(n, P)$ is the special subgroup of $\mathrm{GL}(n, P)$.

LEMMA 32. *Let G be a nilpotent irreducible subgroup of $\mathrm{GL}(n, P)$ of class l. Further, let $E = G_0 \subset G_1 \subset \cdots \subset G_{l-1} \subset G_l = G$ be the upper central series of G. If the factor-group G_2/G_1 contains an element of order n, then G is conjugate in $\mathrm{GL}(n, P)$ to a certain subgroup of Γ_n^l.*

PROOF. We may assume that $G_1 = Z_1$.[19] If aG_1 is an element of order n of the factor-group G_2/G_1, then we can find in G an element b such that $(a, b) = \epsilon E_n$ where ϵ is a primitive nth root of unity. Since P is algebraically closed, a and b can be chosen so that $a^n = E_n$, $|b| = (-1)^{n+1}$. The basis of the space $P^{(n)}$ in which G acts can be chosen so that the matrix a is reduced to

$$\begin{bmatrix} 1 & & & & & \\ & \epsilon & & & & \\ & & \epsilon^2 & & & \\ & & & \ddots & & \\ & & & & & \epsilon^{n-1} \end{bmatrix}$$

and simultaneously the matrix b to

$$h = \begin{bmatrix} 0 & 0 & \cdots & 0 & 1 \\ 1 & 0 & \cdots & 0 & 0 \\ 0 & 1 & \cdots & 0 & 0 \\ \cdot & \cdot & \cdots & \cdot & \cdot \\ \cdot & \cdot & \cdots & \cdot & \cdot \\ 0 & 0 & \cdots & 1 & 0 \end{bmatrix}.$$

For since $a^n = E_n$, a has an eigenvector u_k such that $a(u_k) = \epsilon^k u_k$. From $ab = \epsilon ba$ it follows that $ab^\nu = \epsilon^\nu b^\nu a$. Hence, $ab^\nu(u_k) = \epsilon^\nu b^\nu a(u_k)$, $a[b^\nu(u_k)] = \epsilon^{k+\nu} b^\nu(u_k)$. We set $b^\nu(u_k) = u_{k+\nu}$, $\nu = 1, \cdots, n-1$ (indices to be taken modulo n). Then

[19] See (9).

$b(u_{k+n-1})=\alpha u_k$, $|b|=(-1)^{n+1}\alpha$. Since $|b|=(-1)^{n+1}$, $\alpha=1$. Consequently, $a(u_j)=\epsilon^j u_j$, $b(u_j)=u_{j+1}$, $j=0,1,\cdots,n-1$. In the basis $u_0,u_1,\cdots,u_{n-1}$ a assumes the form

$$c_2=\begin{bmatrix} 1 & & & & \\ & \epsilon & & & \\ & & \epsilon^2 & & \\ & & & \ddots & \\ & & & & \epsilon^{n-1} \end{bmatrix}$$

and b assumes the form

$$h=\begin{bmatrix} 0 & 0 & \cdots & 0 & 1 \\ 1 & 0 & \cdots & 0 & 0 \\ 0 & 1 & \cdots & 0 & 0 \\ \cdot & \cdot & \cdots & \cdot & \cdot \\ \cdot & \cdot & \cdots & \cdot & \cdot \\ 0 & 0 & \cdots & 1 & 0 \end{bmatrix}.$$

Now if $g\in G$, then $(c_2,g)=\epsilon^\alpha=(c_2,h^\alpha)$. Therefore, $g=h^\alpha\phi$, where $(\phi,c_2)=1$. Consequently, $G=(h)\Phi$, where Φ is the centralizer of c_2 in G. Since $\Gamma_n^l=(h)Z_l$, for the proof of the lemma we have to establish that $\Phi\subseteq Z_l$.

Obviously, every matrix of Φ is diagonal. We set $\Phi_j=\Phi\cap G_j$, $j=1,2,\cdots,l$. Then $\Phi_1=\Phi\cap G_1=G_1=Z_1$. Suppose that $\Phi_{j-1}\subseteq Z_{j-1}$. We shall show that $\Phi_j\subseteq Z_j$. For $f_j\in\Phi_j$, $(f_j,h)\in\Phi_{j-1}\subseteq Z_{j-1}$. By construction, Z_j contains f_j. $\Phi_j\subseteq Z_j$. $\Phi_l=\Phi\cap G=\Phi_1\Phi_l\subseteq Z_l$. This proves the lemma.

Let us now apply Theorem 35 and Lemma 32 to the case when n is square-free.

THEOREM 36. *If n is a square-free number, then all the maximal irreducible nilpotent subgroups of* $\mathrm{GL}(n,P)$ *of a given class l are conjugate in* $\mathrm{GL}(n,P)$. *Every irreducible nilpotent subgroup of* $\mathrm{GL}(n,P)$ *of class l is conjugate in* $\mathrm{GL}(n,P)$ *to a certain subgroup of* Γ_n^l.

PROOF. Let n be square-free and Γ an irreducible nilpotent subgroup of $\mathrm{GL}(n,P)$ of class l. By the corollary to Theorem 28 the conditions of Lemma 32 are satisfied for a square-free n. Hence, the theorem follows.

6. **The upper central series.**[20] Let Γ be an irreducible nilpotent subgroup of $\mathrm{GL}(n,P)$, P algebraically closed. Suppose further that $E\subset Z_1\subset\cdots$

[20] §6 is written by R. Tyškevič.

$\subset Z_{l-1} \subset Z_1 = \Gamma$ is the upper central series of Γ. We may assume that $Z_1 = M$, where M is the multiplicative group of the field PE_n (see §3). By Lemma 21, $[Z_2]:P = Z_2:Z_1$. This equation remains true for every subgroup A such that $Z_2 \supseteq A \supseteq Z_1$.

Now let $A \supset Z_1$ be any abelian subgroup of Z_2. Obviously, A is a normal subgroup of Γ and is, therefore, completely reducible. The algebra $[A]$ is a direct sum of fields, $[A]:P = A:Z_1 \leqq n$. The factor-group A/Z_1 can be written in the form of a direct product:

$$A/Z_1 = (a_1 Z_1)(a_2 Z_1)\cdots(a_\nu Z_1),$$

where $a_j Z_1$ is an element of order k_j, k_j/k_i, $j > i$. Since P is algebraically closed, we may set $a_j^{k_j} = 1$,

$$A = (a_1)(a_2)\cdots(a_\nu)Z_1,\ A:Z_1 = k_1 k_2 \cdots k_\nu. \tag{11}$$

LEMMA 33 [22]. *Let F be the centralizer of A in Γ. Then $\Gamma/F \cong A/Z_1$, therefore, $\Gamma:F = A:Z_1 = k_1k_2\cdots k_\nu$. F splits into $\Gamma:F = k_1k_2\cdots k_\nu$ irreducible blocks of degree $n/(k_1k_2\cdots k_\nu)$, and Γ can be represented in the form*

$$\Gamma = (g_1)(g_2)\cdots(g_\nu)F, \tag{12}$$

where

$$(a_j, g_j) = \epsilon_j, \qquad (a_j, g_i) = 1, \qquad i \neq j$$

ϵ_j is a primitive root of the equation $x^{k_j} = 1$.

PROOF. It is easy to see that if b ranges over Γ and a_1 is as in (11), then all commutators (a_1, b) form a cyclic group of order k_1. Therefore, Γ contains an element b_1 such that $(a_1, b_1) = \epsilon_1$ is a primitive root of the equation $x^{k_1} = 1$. Hence, we can represent every element $g \in \Gamma$ in the form $g = b_1^{\alpha 1} f_1$, where f_1 belongs to the centralizer F_1 of a_1 in Γ. $\Gamma = (b_1)F_1$, $\Gamma:F_1 = k_1$, Γ/F_1 is a cyclic group. The derived group (Γ, Γ) of Γ is consequently contained in the centralizer of a_1. But this remains true for every element a_j. Therefore, (Γ, Γ) is contained in the centralizer F of A in Γ, i.e., Γ/F is an abelian group.

We shall now prove at the same time two statements:

1. $\Gamma:F = k_1k_2\cdots k_\nu = A:Z_1$.
2. F splits into $A:Z_1$ irreducible blocks of degree $n/(A:Z_1)$.

For F is the intersection of the ν centralizers of the elements $a_1, a_2, \cdots, a_\nu$ and, by Poincaré's Theorem $\Gamma:F \leqq k_1k_2\cdots k_\nu$. The number s of irreducible blocks of F satisfies the inequality $s \leqq \Gamma:F \leqq k_1k_2\cdots k_\nu$. On the other hand, the rank of the center of the algebra $[F]$ is not greater than the number of blocks of F. But $[A]$ lies in the center of $[F]$, therefore, $[A]:P \leqq s$. Hence,

$$[A]:P=s=\Gamma:F=k_1k_2\cdots k_\nu.$$

We shall now show that Γ can be represented in the form (12). We have seen that $\Gamma=(b_1)F_1$. Obviously, $a_j\in F_1$. In F_1 we choose a matrix b_2 such that the commutator (a_2, b_2) has the greatest order among the commutators (a_2, f_1), $f_1\in F_1$. Obviously, $(a_2, b_2)=\epsilon_2^{\alpha 2}$, $F_1=(b_2)F_2$, where F_2 is the centralizer of a_2 and F_1, $(a_1, b_2)=1$. Proceeding like this several times, we arrive at the equation

$$\Gamma=(b_1)(b_2)\cdots(b_\nu)F,\quad (a_1, b_1)=\epsilon_1,\quad (a_j, b_j)=\epsilon_j^{\alpha j},\quad (a_i, b_j)=1,\quad i<j.$$

The order of (a_j, b_j) is equal to l_j, l_j/k_j, hence, $\Gamma:F=k_1l_2\cdots l_\nu$. But $\Gamma:F=k_1k_2\cdots k_\nu$, consequently, $l_j=k_j$, $(a_j, b_j)=\epsilon_j$. We now have to replace the element b_j by a g_j such that $(a_i, g_j)=1$, $i\neq j$, $(a_i, g_i)=\epsilon_i$.

We set $g_\nu=b_\nu$. Suppose that $b_\nu, b_{\nu-1},\cdots,b_{\nu-k+1}$ have already been replaced by $g_\nu, g_{\nu-1},\cdots,g_{\nu-k+1}$ such that $(a_j, g_j)=\epsilon_j^{\delta ij}$, $\nu\geqq i\geqq \nu-k+1$. Then we shall show that a suitable replacement can also be made for $b_{\nu-k}$. $(a_j, b_{\nu-k})=1, j<\nu-k$; $(a_{\nu-k}, b_{\nu-k})=\epsilon_{\nu-k}$; $(a_j, b_{\nu-k})=\epsilon_j^{\alpha j}$, $j>\nu$.

For $g_{\nu-k}$ we choose $g_{\nu-k}=b_{\nu-k}g_{\nu-k+1}^{-\alpha_{\nu-k+1}}\cdots g_\nu^{-\alpha_\nu}$; then $(a_{\nu-k}, g_{\nu-k})=\epsilon_{\nu-k}$, $(a_j, g_{\nu-k})=1$, $j\neq\nu-k$. Equation (12) is now proved.

It remains to prove the isomorphism $\Gamma/F\cong A/Z_1$. From (12) we find $\Gamma/F=(g_1F)(g_2F)\cdots(g_\nu F)$, g_jF is of order k_j. Γ/F is abelian and $\Gamma:F=k_1k_2\cdots k_\nu$. Consequently, $(g_1F)(g_2F)\cdots(g_\nu F)$ is the direct product of cyclic groups of order $k_1, k_2,\cdots,k_\nu$, i.e., $\Gamma/F\cong A/Z_1$. The lemma is now proved.

LEMMA 34. *The matrices* $a_1, a_2,\cdots,a_\nu$ *and* $g_1, g_2,\cdots,g_\nu$ *can be chosen in the following way*:

$$\begin{aligned} a_1&=b_{k_1}\times E_{n/k_1}\\ a_2&=E_{k_1}\times b_{k_2}\times E_{n/(k_1k_2)},\\ &\vdots\\ a_\nu&=E_{k_1\cdots k_{\nu-1}}\times b_{k_\nu}\times E_{n/(k_1\cdots k_\nu)}, \end{aligned}\tag{13}$$

$$\begin{aligned} g_1&=f_1(h_{k_1}\times E_{n/k_1}),\\ g_2&=f_2(E_{k_1}\times h_{k_2}\times E_{n/(k_1k_2)}),\\ &\vdots\\ g_\nu&=f_\nu(E_{k_1\cdots k_{\nu-1}}\times h_{k_\nu}\times E_{n/(k_1\cdots k_\nu)}), \end{aligned}\tag{14}$$

where f_i, $i=1,2,\cdots,\nu$, *is a matrix of the form*

$$\begin{bmatrix} \phi_1^i & & & \\ & \phi_2^i & & \\ & & \ddots & \\ & & & \phi_{k_1\cdots k_\nu}^i \end{bmatrix}$$

ϕ_j^i a matrix of degree $n/(k_1\cdots k_\nu)$,

$$b_{k_j} = \begin{bmatrix} 1 & & & & \\ & \epsilon_j & & & \\ & & \epsilon_j^2 & & \\ & & & \ddots & \\ & & & & \epsilon_j^{k_j-1} \end{bmatrix}, \qquad h_{k_j} = \begin{bmatrix} 0 & 0 & \cdots & 0 & 1 \\ 1 & 0 & \cdots & 0 & 0 \\ 0 & 1 & \cdots & 0 & 0 \\ \cdot & \cdot & \cdots & \cdot & \cdot \\ \cdot & \cdot & \cdots & \cdot & \cdot \\ 0 & 0 & \cdots & 1 & 0 \end{bmatrix}$$

is a matrix of degree k_j.

PROOF. Let $C=(a_1)(a_2)\cdots(a_\nu)$. As an abstract group C is determined by the numbers $k_1, k_2, \cdots, k_\nu$. The trace of every element $d \in C$ other than the unit element is equal to zero, because the eigenvalues of $d \in C$ are roots of unity and are repeated equally often. Hence, it follows that the group C is uniquely determined to within conjugacy in $\mathrm{GL}(n, P)$ by the numbers $k_1, k_2, \cdots, k_\nu$. The group

$$C' = (b_{k_1} \times E_{n/k_1}) \cdots (E_{k_1\cdots k_{\nu-1}} \times b_{k_\nu} \times E_{n/(k_1\cdots k_\nu)})$$

is isomorphic to C and the same relations hold for the traces of its elements. Therefore, C and C' are conjugate in $\mathrm{GL}(n, P)$. The equation (14) now follows from (13) and the commutator conditions of Lemma 33. This proves the lemma.

Now let Γ be maximal among the nilpotent subgroups of $\mathrm{GL}(n, P)$ of class l. We represent it in the form $\Gamma=(g_1)F_1$, where $(a_1, g_1)=\epsilon_1$, a_1Z_1 is an element of maximal order k_1 of the factor-group Z_2/Z_1, ϵ_1 a primitive root of the equation $x^{k_1}=1$. We reduce the matrices a_1 and g_1 to the form:

$$a_1 = b_{k_1} \times E_{n/k_1}, \qquad g_1 = \begin{bmatrix} \phi_1 & & & \\ & \phi_2 & & \\ & & \ddots & \\ & & & \phi_{k_1} \end{bmatrix} (h_{k_1} \times E_{n/k_1}).$$

If f_1 ranges over F_1, then

$$f_1=\begin{bmatrix}\psi_1 & & & \\ & \psi_2 & & \\ & & \ddots & \\ & & & \psi_{k_1}\end{bmatrix},$$

where the mapping $f_1\to\psi_i$ is an irreducible representation of degree n/k_1, $i=1,2,\cdots,k_1$. Let us construct the auxiliary sequence of abelian subgroups of $\mathrm{GL}(k_1,P)$

$$E\subset B_1\subset B_2\subset\cdots\subset B_j\subset\cdots,$$

where $B_1=M$, $B_2=(b_{k_1})B_1,\cdots,B_j,\cdots$ is a set of diagonal matrices whose commutators with h_{k_1} are contained in B_{j-1}. We know already that $B_j=(c_j)B_{j-1}$, $c_j^{k_1}\in B_{j-1}$. The matrices c_j can be chosen so that $(c_j,\ h)=c_{j-1}$ (see §5).

We set $d_i=c_i\times E_{n/k_1}$.

LEMMA 35. *Let Z_j be the first of the hypercenters of Γ containing matrices that do not commute with a_1. Then $d_i\in Z_i\setminus Z_{i-1}$ for $i\leqq j$ and $d_{j+1}\notin\Gamma$.*

PROOF. $d_2=a_1\in Z_2\setminus Z_1$. Suppose that $d_i\in Z_i\setminus Z_{i-1}$ for all $i<t\leqq j$. We shall show that $d_t\in Z_t\setminus Z_{t-1}$. Since $(d_t,\ f_1)=1$ for every $f_1\in F_1$, it is sufficient to show that $(d_t,\ g_1)\in Z_{t-1}\setminus Z_{t-2}$. But

$$(d_t,g_1)=(c_t\times E_{n/k_1},\begin{bmatrix}\phi_1 & & & \\ & \phi_2 & & \\ & & \ddots & \\ & & & \phi_{k_1}\end{bmatrix}(h_{k_1}\times E_{n/k_1}))$$

$$=(c_t,\ h_{k_1})\times E_{n/k_1}=c_{t-1}\times E_{n/k_1}=d_{t-1}\in Z_{t-1}\setminus Z_{t-2}.$$

Let us also show that $d_{j+1}\notin\Gamma$. A matrix $u\in Z_j$ that does not commute with a_1 has the form $u=g_1^{\alpha 1}f_1$, $\alpha_1\not\equiv 0\ (\mathrm{mod}\, k_1)$. If $g\in\Gamma$, then $(g,\ u)\in Z_{j-1}$. But

$$(d_{j+1},u)=(c_{j+1}\times E_{n/k_1},\begin{bmatrix}\psi_1 & & & \\ & \psi_2 & & \\ & & \ddots & \\ & & & \psi_{k_1}\end{bmatrix}(h_{k_1}^{\alpha 1}\times E_{n/k_1}))$$

$$=(c_{j+1},\ h_{k_1}^{\alpha 1})\times E_{n/k_1}=c_j^{\alpha 1}b\times E_{n/k_1},\ b\in B_{j-1},\ c_j\in B_j\setminus B_{j-1}.$$

Since $\alpha_1 \not\equiv 0 \pmod{k_1}$, we have $(d_{j+1}, u) \in Z_j \setminus Z_{j-1}$. The lemma is now proved.

LEMMA 36. $Z_{l-1} \subset F_1$.

PROOF. Let Z_j be the first of the hypercenters of Γ not entirely contained in F_1. From the preceding lemma it then follows that $d_j \in Z_j$ and $d_{j+1} \notin \Gamma$. If we had $j \neq l$, then the group $G = (d_{j+1})\Gamma$ would be nilpotent of class l, but this is impossible. Consequently, $j = l$.

From Lemma 36 we immediately deduce

THEOREM 37. *If Z_j is irreducible, then $Z_j = \Gamma$, i.e., Γ is a nilpotent group of class j.*

THEOREM 38. *Z_{l-1} is contained in the centralizer F of Z_2 in Γ.*

PROOF. Suppose that $d \in Z_{l-1}$ and $c \in Z_2$ are such that $(c, d) = 1$. Let the order of cZ_1 be equal to $k_2 < k_1$ and p a prime number occurring in k_1 with an exponent α and in k_2 with an exponent β, $\alpha > \beta$. Then the order of the element $ca_1^{k_1/(p^\alpha)} Z_1$ is equal to $p^{\alpha-\beta} k_2$. Hence, it follows that among all the elements of Z_2 that do not commute with d there is an element of order k_1. The latter contradicts the statement of Lemma 36.

A corollary of Theorem 38 is

THEOREM 39. *If $l > 2$, then Z_2 is an abelian group.*

Lemmas 34, 35, 36 and Theorems 37, 38, 39 were proved by R. Tyškevič.

7. **Locally nilpotent irreducible subgroups of** GL(n, P) [**21**]. A group Γ is called locally nilpotent if every finite set of elements of Γ generates a nilpotent group.

Let P be an algebraically closed field. We examine irreducible locally nilpotent subgroup Γ of GL(n, P). We shall assume that $\Gamma \supset M$, where M is the multiplicative group of PE_n. It is easy to see that Γ can be represented in the form

$$\Gamma = \Gamma_0 M, \tag{15}$$

where $\Gamma_0 = \Gamma \cap \mathrm{SL}(n, P)$ (see Proof of Theorem 29). Γ_0 is obviously an irreducible locally nilpotent subgroup of SL(n, P).

LEMMA 37. *The group* $\Gamma_0 = \Gamma \cap \mathrm{SL}(n, P)$ *is locally finite. The set of all prime divisors of the orders of its elements coincides with the set of all prime divisors of* n.

PROOF. Since Γ_0 is irreducible, we can find in it n^2 linearly independent matrices $g_1, g_2, \cdots, g_{n^2}$. Now if $a_1, \cdots, a_s$ are arbitrary elements of Γ_0, then the group A_0 generated by them is contained in the irreducible nilpotent group $H_0 < \mathrm{SL}(n, P)$ generated by the matrices $a_1, \cdots, a_s, g_1, \cdots, g_{n^2}$.
By Theorem 29, H_0 is a finite group and the order of H_0 and n have the same prime divisors. Hence, both statements of Lemma 37 follow.

LEMMA 38. *A locally nilpotent irreducible subgroup* Γ *of* $\mathrm{GL}(n, P)$ *is conjugate in* $\mathrm{GL}(n, P)$ *to a certain monomial group, i.e.,* $P^{(n)}$ *has a basis* $u_1, \cdots, u_n$ *such that for every* $g \in \Gamma$

$$g(u_1) = \gamma_1 u_{i_1}, \cdots, g(u_n) = \gamma_n u_{i_n}, \quad \gamma_j \in P, \tag{16}$$

where $i_1, \cdots, i_n$ *is a permutation of the numbers* $1, 2, \cdots, n$.

PROOF. It is sufficient to show that for $n > 1$ the group Γ is imprimitive (see the proof of Theorem 24). We may assume that Γ contains M (M is the multiplicative group of the field PE_n). Suppose that Γ is primitive; then M is a maximal abelian normal subgroup of Γ. The index of M in Γ is finite (see Chapter I, §3). Since $\Gamma = \Gamma_0 M$ and $\Gamma_0 = \Gamma \cap \mathrm{SL}(n, P)$, therefore Γ_0 is a finite nilpotent irreducible group. Thus $\Gamma = \Gamma_0 M$ is also a nilpotent irreducible group. By Theorem 24 Γ is primitive only when $n = 1$. This proves the lemma.

Suppose now that $n = p^\nu$, where p is a prime number. We shall construct one locally nilpotent irreducible subgroup Γ_{p^ν} of $\mathrm{GL}(p^\nu, P)$, assuming that the characteristic of P is not p. In $P^{(n)}$ ($n = p^\nu$) we choose an arbitrary basis $u_1, \cdots, u_n$. We set

$$\Gamma_{p^\nu} = N_{p^\nu} H_{p^\nu} M \tag{17}$$

where (1) M is the multiplicative group of PE_n;

(2) H_{p^ν} consists of all those h for which $h(u_j) = \eta_j \mu_j$, $\eta^{p^\mu} = 1$, $\eta_j \in P$, $j = 1, \cdots, n$.[21]

(3) N_{p^ν} is a maximal transitive nilpotent subgroup of the symmetric group S_{p^ν} permuting $u_1, \cdots, u_n$.

It is easy to verify that Γ_{p^ν} is, in fact, locally nilpotent. For $N_{p^\nu} H_{p^\nu}$ is a

[21] H_{p^ν} is obviously the direct product of n groups of type p^∞.

locally finite p-group. Therefore Γ_{p^ν} is locally nilpotent. We recall that in S_{p^ν} the maximal nilpotent transitive subgroups are conjugate (see Theorem 26).

LEMMA 39. *Every locally nilpotent irreducible subgroup of* $\mathrm{GL}(p^\nu, P)$ *is conjugate in* $\mathrm{GL}(p^\nu, P)$ *to a certain subgroup of* Γ_{p^ν} *(see* (17)).

PROOF. Let Γ be an arbitrary irreducible locally nilpotent subgroup of $\mathrm{GL}(p^\nu, P)$. We may assume that $M \subset \Gamma$. Then $\Gamma = \Gamma_0 M$, where $\Gamma_0 = \Gamma \cap \mathrm{SL}(p^\nu, P)$. By Lemma 37 Γ_0 is a locally finite irreducible p-group. By Lemma 38, $P^{(n)}$ $(n = p^\nu)$ contains a basis $u_1, \cdots, u_n$ such that for $g \in \Gamma$ we have $g(u_1) = \gamma_1 u_{i_1}, \cdots, g(u_n) = \gamma_n u_{i_n}$, $\gamma_j \in P$, $i_1, \cdots, i_n$ a permutation of the numbers $1, 2, \cdots, n$. In Γ_0 we choose n elements $g_1, g_2, \cdots, g_n$ such that $g_1(u_1) = u_1, g_2(u_1) = \beta_2 u_2, \cdots, g_n(u_1) = \beta_n u_n$, $\beta_j \in P$.

Now we change the basis of $P^{(n)}$ somewhat: instead of $u_1, u_2, \cdots, u_n$ we choose $v_1, v_2, \cdots, v_n$, where $v_1 = u_1$, $v_2 = g_2(u_1), \cdots, v_n = g_n(u_1)$. Suppose now that $a \in \Gamma_0$; then $a(v_\rho) = \alpha_\rho v_{i_\rho}$, $\rho = 1, \cdots, n$. We shall show that α_ρ is a root of an equation of the form $x^{p^\mu} = 1$. It is easy to verify that $g_\rho g_{i_\rho}^{-1} a(v_\rho) = \alpha_\rho v_\rho$, $b = g_\rho g_{i_\rho}^{-1} a \in \Gamma_0$, $b^{p^\mu} = E_n$. Therefore $b^{p^\mu}(v_\rho) = \alpha_\rho^{p^\mu} v_\rho = v_\rho$, $\alpha^{p^\mu} = 1$.

Thus $a \in \Gamma_0$ can be represented in the form $a = th$, where $h(v_\rho) = \alpha_\rho v_\rho$, $h \in H_{p^\nu}$, $t \in N_{p^\nu}$. Hence, $\Gamma_0 \subset N_{p^\nu} H_{p^\nu}$, $\Gamma = \Gamma_0 M \subseteq \Gamma_{p^\nu} = N_{p^\nu} H_{p^\nu} M$. The lemma is now proved.

COROLLARY. Γ_{p^ν} *is a maximal locally nilpotent subgroup of* $\mathrm{GL}(p^\nu, P)$. *All maximal irreducible locally nilpotent subgroups of* $\mathrm{GL}(p^\nu, P)$ *are conjugate.*

Later we shall show the conjugacy of the maximal locally nilpotent irreducible subgroups of $\mathrm{GL}(n, P)$ for an arbitrary n.

First of all we introduce one irreducible locally nilpotent subgroup Γ_n of $\mathrm{GL}(n, P)$.

Let $n = p_1^{\nu 1} \cdots p_k^{\nu k}$, where p_j are distinct prime numbers, $k > 1$. By Γ_n we denote the group of all matrices of the form

$$\lambda \sigma_1 \times \cdots \times \sigma_k \qquad (18)$$

where λ is an arbitrary nonzero element of P, σ_j an arbitrary matrix of $N_{p_j}^{\nu j} H_{p_j}^{\nu j}$ (see (17)). It is obvious that Γ_n is locally nilpotent.

Now let us proceed to prove that every irreducible locally nilpotent subgroup Γ of $\mathrm{GL}(n, P)$ is conjugate in $\mathrm{GL}(n, P)$ to a certain subgroup of Γ_n. We shall assume that $M \subset \Gamma$. Then $\Gamma = \Gamma_0 M$, where $\Gamma_0 = \Gamma \cap \mathrm{SL}(n, P)$. The group Γ_0 is an irreducible locally nilpotent locally finite group. The set of prime divisors of the orders of its elements consists of all prime divisors of n (see Lemma 37). Therefore, Γ_0 splits into the direct product of k p_j-groups $\Pi_{01}, \cdots, \Pi_{0k}$, where Π_{0j} is a Sylow p_j-subgroup of Γ_0.

Let us examine the last factor Π_{0k}. This factor Π_{0k} is reducible and all irreducible blocks of Π_{0k} have one and the same dimension $m=p_k^{\alpha}$, $\alpha \leqq \nu_k$. We write Γ_0 in the form $\Gamma_0=H_0\Pi_{0k}$, where $H_0=\Pi_{01}\cdots\Pi_{0k-1}$.

It is clear that $P^{(n)}$ can be represented as follows:

$$P^{(n)}=L_1+h_2(L_1)+\cdots+h_{n/m}(L_1),$$

where $h_j \in H_0$, and L_1, $L_j=h_j(L_1)$, $j=2, \cdots, n/m$ are irreducible subspaces of $P^{(n)}$, invariant with respect to Π_{0k}. Thus Π_{0k} induces in $L_1, \cdots, L_{n/m}$ equivalent irreducible representations. For let $v_1, \cdots, v_m$ be an arbitrary basis of L_1; then we choose as basis of the subspace $L_j=h_j(L_1)$ the vectors $u_1=h_j(v_1), \cdots, u_m=h_j(v_m)$. If $f\in\Pi_{0k}$, $f(v_i)=\alpha_i^t v_t$, then $f(u_i)=fh_j(v_i)=h_jf(v_i)=h_j(\alpha_i^t v_t)=\alpha_i^t u_t$.

In the basis $v_1, \cdots, v_m, \cdots, u_1, \cdots, u_m, \cdots, f\in\Pi_{0k}$ assumes the form

$$f=\begin{pmatrix} \sigma_k & & & & \\ & \sigma_k & & & \\ & & \cdot & & \\ & & & \cdot & \\ & & & & \sigma_k \end{pmatrix}=E_{n/m}\times\sigma_k,$$

where σ_k is a matrix of order $m=p_k^{\alpha}$.

The matrices $h\in H_0$ are permutable with every matrix f and, consequently, have the form $h=\tau\times E_m$, where τ is a matrix of order n/m.

It is easy to verify that the representation

$$h\rightarrow\tau \tag{19}$$

is irreducible. Therefore, only the prime numbers $p_1, p_2, \cdots, p_{k-1}$ occur in n/m, i.e., $m=p_k^{\nu_k}$, $n/m=p_1^{\nu_1}p_2^{\nu_2}\cdots p_{k-1}^{\nu_{k-1}}$.

Thus $g\in\Gamma_0$ can be written as

$$g=\tau\times\sigma_k, \quad \sigma_k\in N_{p_k^{\nu_k}}H_{p_k^{\nu_k}}.$$

When we proceed in the same way with the group T over which the matrices τ range (see (19)), we arrive at the equation $\tau=\tau_1\times\sigma_{k-1}$, where $\sigma_{k-1}\in N_{p_{k-1}^{\nu_{k-1}}}H_{p_{k-1}^{\nu_{k-1}}}$ and τ_1 ranges over precisely the irreducible representations of degree $p_1^{\nu_1}\cdots p_{k-2}^{\nu_{k-2}}$ of the group $\Pi_{01}\cdot\Pi_{02}\cdots\Pi_{0,k-2}$.

Such arguments lead us to the equation

$$g=\sigma_1\times\sigma_2\times\cdots\times\sigma_k, \quad g\in\Gamma_0, \qquad \sigma_j\in N_{p_j^{\nu_j}}H_{p_j^{\nu_j}}.$$

Therefore $\Gamma=\Gamma_0M$ is conjugate to a certain subgroup of Γ_n.

Thus we have come to the following theorem.

THEOREM 40. *All the maximal locally nilpotent irreducible subgroups of* $\mathrm{GL}(n, P)$ *are conjugate to each other in* $\mathrm{GL}(n, P)$. *The matrices of a maximal locally nilpotent irreducible subgroup of* $\mathrm{GL}(n, P)$ *can be reduced simultaneously to the form* (18).

8. **Reducible nilpotent and locally nilpotent subgroups of the full linear group.** We shall assume that P is an algebraically closed field.

1. THEOREM 41. *If a nilpotent group* $\Gamma \subset \mathrm{GL}(n, P)$ *consists of matrices of the form*

$$g = \begin{bmatrix} a_g & b_g \\ 0 & c_g \end{bmatrix}, \tag{20}$$

where $g \to a_g$ and $g \to c_g$ are irreducible inequivalent representations of Γ, then Γ is completely reducible. First we shall prove

LEMMA 40. *In a group* Γ *satisfying the conditions of Theorem* 41 *there are no matrices of the form*

$$h = \begin{bmatrix} E_m & B_{ml} \\ 0 & E_l \end{bmatrix}, \tag{21}$$

where $B_{ml} \neq 0$.

PROOF OF THE LEMMA. Suppose that h of the form (21) belongs to Γ. The commutator (g, h), where $g \in \Gamma$, is either equal to the unit element or is also of the form (21). Since Γ is nilpotent, Γ contains, together with h, a matrix $h_1 \neq E_n$ of the form (21) such that $(g, h_1) = E_n$ for every $g \in \Gamma$. If

$$h_1 = \begin{bmatrix} E_m & b \\ 0 & E_l \end{bmatrix} \quad \text{and} \quad g = \begin{bmatrix} a_g & b_g \\ 0 & c_g \end{bmatrix},$$

then

$$(g, h_1) = \begin{bmatrix} E_m & a_g b c_g^{-1} - b \\ 0 & E_l \end{bmatrix}.$$

From the condition $(g, h_1) = E_n$ we obtain $a_g b = b c_g$. By Schur's Lemma, $b = 0$, but this contradicts the choice of h_1. The lemma is proved.

Now we proceed to the proof of the theorem. We may assume that Γ contains the multiplicative group M of the field PE_n.

Two cases are possible:
(i) in Γ there is a matrix of the form

$$f=\begin{bmatrix} \lambda_1 E_m & b \\ 0 & \lambda_2 E_l \end{bmatrix}, \qquad \lambda_1, \lambda_2 \in P, \quad \lambda_1 \neq \lambda_2; \tag{22}$$

(ii) there are no matrices of the form (22) in Γ.

In the first case we consider the commutator (g, f), where $g \in \Gamma$. Obviously, (g, f) is either equal to the unit element or is of the form (21). By Lemma 40, the second possibility cannot occur. Therefore, $(g, f) = E_n$. Thus all the matrices $g \in \Gamma$ are permutable with f. But

$$sfs^{-1} = \begin{bmatrix} \lambda_1 E_m & 0 \\ 0 & \lambda_2 E_l \end{bmatrix} = f_1$$

if

$$s = \begin{bmatrix} E_m & T \\ 0 & E_l \end{bmatrix}, \qquad T = (\lambda_1 - \lambda_2)^{-1} b.$$

The matrices $s\Gamma s^{-1}$ are permutable with f_1. Therefore, they have the form $\begin{bmatrix} a_g & 0 \\ 0 & c_g \end{bmatrix}$, and Γ is completely reducible.

Suppose now that there are no matrices of the form (22) in Γ. By Theorem 27 there exists an integer μ such that

$$g^{\mu} = \begin{bmatrix} \lambda_1 E_m & b \\ 0 & \lambda_2 E_l \end{bmatrix}, \qquad \lambda_1, \lambda_2 \in P \tag{23}$$

for every $g \in \Gamma$. Since by assumption there are no matrices of the form (22) in Γ, we have $\lambda_1 = \lambda_2 = \lambda$. Furthermore, by Lemma 40, $b = 0$. Therefore, instead of (23) we can write

$$g^{\mu} = \lambda E_n. \tag{24}$$

Since $\Gamma \supset M$, $\Gamma = \Gamma_0 M$, where $\Gamma_0 = \Gamma \cap \mathrm{SL}(n, P)$. If $g \in \Gamma_0$, then $g^{\mu} = \lambda E_n$, where $\lambda^n = 1$. Obviously, λ is a primitive root of the equation $x^k = 1$, where k is not divisible by the characteristic of P. Therefore,[22] Γ_0 is a finite group whose order is not divisible by the characteristic of P. From this the complete reducibility of Γ follows.

THEOREM 42. *Suppose that a nilpotent group $\Gamma \subset \mathrm{GL}(n, P)$ consists of matrices of the form*

[22] See [**12**, Lemma 1].

$$g=\begin{bmatrix} a_g & b_g \\ 0 & a_g \end{bmatrix} \tag{25}$$

where $g \to a_g$ is an irreducible representation of Γ. Then $\mathrm{GL}(n, P)$ contains a matrix s such that $sgs^{-1}=\begin{bmatrix} a_g & \lambda a_g \\ 0 & a_g \end{bmatrix}$, where $\lambda \in P$ for all $g \in \Gamma$.

To begin with, we give two lemmas.

LEMMA 41. *The matrices of the center Z of Γ are of the form:*

$$c=\begin{bmatrix} \lambda E_m & \mu E_m \\ 0 & \lambda E_m \end{bmatrix}=\begin{bmatrix} \lambda & \mu \\ 0 & \lambda \end{bmatrix} \times E_m.$$

LEMMA 42. *If*

$$\begin{bmatrix} \lambda E_m & b \\ 0 & \lambda E_m \end{bmatrix} \in \Gamma, \qquad \lambda \in P,$$

then $b \in PE_m$.

Lemma 41 can be proved by a direct verification.

PROOF OF LEMMA 42. Suppose that $f=\begin{bmatrix} E_m & b \\ 0 & E_m \end{bmatrix}$ belongs to Γ, $b \notin PE_m$. Since Γ is nilpotent, Γ contains together with f also a matrix $f_1=\begin{bmatrix} E_m & b_1 \\ 0 & E_m \end{bmatrix}$ such that $b_1 \notin PE_m$, but $(g, f_1)=\begin{bmatrix} E_m & \mu E_m \\ 0 & E_m \end{bmatrix}$, $\mu \in P$ for every $g \in \Gamma$.

By Lemma 41, $f_1 \notin Z$. Therefore, we can find in Γ a matrix $g=\begin{bmatrix} a & d \\ 0 & a \end{bmatrix}$ such that

$$gf_1g^{-1}f_1^{-1}=\begin{bmatrix} E_m & \mu E_m \\ 0 & E_m \end{bmatrix}, \qquad \mu \in P, \ \mu \neq 0. \tag{26}$$

An easy computation gives

$$(g, f_1)=\begin{bmatrix} E_m & ab_1a^{-1}-b_1 \\ 0 & E_m \end{bmatrix}.$$

Therefore, $ab_1a^{-1}-b_1=\mu E_m$. Taking traces we obtain $\mathrm{tr}(ab_1a^{-1}-b_1)=m\mu$. Hence, $m\mu=0$. Since m is not divisible by the characteristic of P (see Theorem 28, Corollary 2), $\mu=0$. But this contradicts (26) and the lemma is proved.

PROOF OF THEOREM 42. We may assume that the center Z of Γ consists of all nonsingular matrices of the form $\begin{bmatrix} \lambda & \mu \\ 0 & \lambda \end{bmatrix} \times E_m$. The matrices a_g (see (25)) range over an irreducible nilpotent group A of degree m. The group A can be represented in the form $A = A_0 M$, where A_0 is a finite group and M the multiplicative group of P. Therefore, Γ can be represented in the form

$$\Gamma = \Gamma_0 M,$$

where Γ_0 consists of the matrices

$$g_0 = \begin{bmatrix} a_0 & b \\ 0 & a_0 \end{bmatrix}, \qquad a_0 \in A_0.$$

Γ_0 has a normal subgroup C of finite index consisting of all the matrices of the form

$$\begin{bmatrix} 1 & \mu \\ 0 & 1 \end{bmatrix} \times E_m. \tag{27}$$

For the matrices (27) form the kernel of the homomorphism

$$g_0 \to a_0.$$

Therefore, $\Gamma_0 : C$ coincides with the order of A_0. In every coset of C in Γ there is one and only one element of finite order, prime to the characteristic of P. For suppose that

$$g_0 = \begin{bmatrix} a_0 & b \\ 0 & a_0 \end{bmatrix} \in \Gamma$$

and t is the order of a_0. By Lemma 42,

$$g_0^t = \begin{bmatrix} E_m & \mu E_m \\ 0 & E_m \end{bmatrix}, \qquad \mu \in P.$$

If $\alpha \in P$, then

$$\begin{bmatrix} E_m & \alpha E_m \\ 0 & E_m \end{bmatrix}^t = \begin{bmatrix} E_m & \alpha t E_m \\ 0 & E_m \end{bmatrix}.$$

Further,

$$\left(g_0 \begin{bmatrix} E_m & \alpha E_m \\ 0 & E_m \end{bmatrix} \right)^t = \begin{bmatrix} E_m & (\mu + \alpha t)\, E_m \\ 0 & E_m \end{bmatrix}.$$

Since t is not divisible by the characteristic of P, α can be chosen so that

$\alpha t+\mu=0$. By this relation, α is uniquely determined. Thus, every coset of C in Γ_0 contains one and only one element $\bar{a}_0$ of finite order prime to the characteristic of P. All these elements $\bar{a}_0$ form a finite subgroup $\bar{A}_0$ of Γ_0 (see A. G. Kuroš [7, Volume 2, p. 413]). Obviously, $\Gamma_0=\bar{A}_0 C$. The finite group $\bar{A}_0$ is completely reducible; there exists a matrix $s=\begin{bmatrix} E_m & R \\ 0 & E_m \end{bmatrix}$ such that for every $\bar{a}_0 \in \bar{A}_0$

$$s\bar{a}_0 s^{-1}=\begin{bmatrix} a_0 & 0 \\ 0 & a_0 \end{bmatrix}.$$

Every matrix $\begin{bmatrix} E_m & \mu E_m \\ 0 & E_m \end{bmatrix}$ of C remains unchanged under transformation with s. Therefore, the matrices of the group $s\Gamma_0 s^{-1}$ are of the form

$$\begin{bmatrix} a_0 & \mu a_0 \\ 0 & a_0 \end{bmatrix}.$$

Hence, the theorem follows.

Note that in Theorems 41 and 42 the matrix transforming the group Γ can be chosen in the form

$$s=\begin{bmatrix} E_m & R \\ 0 & E_l \end{bmatrix}.$$

2. We now give, without proof, statements that generalize Theorems 41 and 42.

THEOREM 43. *Let Γ be a reducible nilpotent subgroup of $\mathrm{GL}(n,P)$ and suppose that all the matrices g of Γ can be reduced simultaneously to the form*

$$g=\begin{bmatrix} a^g & a_{12}^g & \cdots & a_{1k}^g \\ 0 & a^g & \cdots & a_{2k}^g \\ \cdot & \cdot & \cdots & \cdot \\ \cdot & \cdot & \cdots & \cdot \\ 0 & 0 & \cdots & a^g \end{bmatrix}, \tag{28}$$

where $g\to a^g$ is an irreducible representation of Γ.

Then there exists a matrix T such that for all $g\in\Gamma$

$$TgT^{-1}=c^g\times a^g,$$

where

$$c^g = \begin{bmatrix} 1 & \lambda_{12}^g & \cdots & \lambda_{1k}^g \\ 0 & 1 & \cdots & \lambda_{2k}^g \\ \cdot & \cdot & \cdots & \cdot \\ \cdot & \cdot & \cdots & \cdot \\ 0 & 0 & \cdots & 1 \end{bmatrix}, \qquad \lambda_{ij} \in P \tag{29}$$

$$T = \begin{bmatrix} E_m & t_{12} & \cdots & t_{1k} \\ 0 & E_m & \cdots & t_{2k} \\ \cdot & \cdot & \cdots & \cdot \\ \cdot & \cdot & \cdots & \cdot \\ 0 & 0 & \cdots & E_m \end{bmatrix}, \qquad k = n/m \tag{30}$$

(*compare with Theorem* 42).

Now let Γ be an arbitrary reducible nilpotent group acting in $P^{(n)}$.

THEOREM 44. *The space $P^{(n)}$ can be represented in the form of a direct sum of subspaces invariant under Γ such that Γ induces in each of them a quasi-triangular group with equivalent irreducible parts* (*compare with Theorem* 41).

The following theorem completely describes all the maximal locally nilpotent subgroups of GL(n, P).[23]

THEOREM 45. *Let Γ be a maximal locally nilpotent subgroup of* GL(n, P). *Then the space $P^{(n)}$ splits into the direct sum of invariant subspaces relative to Γ,*

$$P^{(n)} = Q_1 \dot{+} Q_2 \dot{+} \cdots \dot{+} Q_\nu,$$

such that Γ induces in each Q_j a group Γ_j whose irreducible parts are all equivalent; the group Γ_j having k_j irreducible equivalent parts of degree m_j consists of all the matrices of the form

$$c \times a,$$

where a ranges over a maximal irreducible locally nilpotent subgroup of GL(m_j, P), *c is an arbitrary triangular matrix of order k_j with unit elements in the diagonal.*

Since GL(m, P) contains to within conjugacy only one maximal irreducible locally nilpotent subgroup, by Theorem 45 every maximal locally nilpotent subgroup of GL(n, P) is given to within equivalence in GL(n, P)

[23] The irreducible maximal locally nilpotent subgroups of GL(n, P) are described in Theorem 40.

by a representation of the number n in the form

$$n = k_1 m_1 + k_2 m_2 + \cdots + k_\nu m_\nu.$$

THEOREM 46. $\mathrm{GL}(n, P)$ *contains only a finite number of inconjugate maximal nilpotent subgroups (reducible and irreducible) of a fixed class of nilpotency* $l \geqq n-1$.

Theorems 41 and 42 were published in the paper [**24**] of the author. Theorems 43-46 were proved jointly by the author and R. I. Tyškevič.

Bibliography*

1. C. Jordan, *Traité des substitutions et équations algébriques,* Paris, 1870.

2. E. Galois, *Collected works,* ONTI, Moscow, 1936. (Russian)

3. B. L. van der Waerden, *Modern algebra,* 2nd ed., Springer, Berlin, 1937; Russian transl., OGIZ, Moscow, 1947.

4. ———, *Gruppen von linearen Transformationen,* Springer, Berlin, 1935.

5. H. Weyl, *The classical groups, their invariants and representations,* Princeton Univ. Press, Princeton, N. J., 1939; Russian transl., IL, Moscow, 1947.

6. O. Ju Šmidt, *Abstract theory of groups,* 2nd ed., Moscow, 1933. (Russian)

7. A. G. Kuroš, *Theory of groups,* 2nd ed., GITTL, Moscow, 1953 (Russian); English transl., Chelsea, New York, 1955, 1956.

8. L. E. Dickenson, *Linear groups,* Leipzig, 1901.

9. C. Jordan, *Sur la resolution algébrique des equations primitives de dégré* p^2, J. Math. Pures Appl. **12**(1868).

10. ———, *Sur les groupes résolubles,* J. Math. Pures Appl. **1917,** 263-274.

11. A. H. Clifford, *Representations induced in an invariant subgroup,* Ann. of Math. (2) **38**(1937), 533-550.

12. A. I. Mal'cev, *On some classes of infinite soluble groups,* Mat. Sb. (N.S.) **28(70)** (1951), 567-588. (Russian)

13. A. G. Kuroš and S. N. Černikov, *Solvable and nilpotent groups,* Uspehi Mat. Nauk **2**(1947), no. 3(19), 18-59 (Russian); English transl., Amer. Math. Soc. Transl. No. 80 (1953); reprint, (1) **1**(1962), 283-338.

14. D. Suprunenko, *Primitive solvable groups of substitutions,* Mat. Sb. (N.S.) **20(62)** (1947), 331-350. (Russian)

15. ———, *Soluble groups of matrices,* Belorussk. Gos. Univ. Učen. Zap. Ser. Fiz.-Mat. **1951**, no. 12, 74-112. (Russian)

16. ———, *Soluble groups of matrices,* Dokl. Akad. Nauk SSSR **83**(1952), 183-186. (Russian)

17. ———, *On nilpotent matrix groups,* Belorussk. Gos. Univ. Učen. Zap. Ser. Fiz.-Mat. **1953**, no. 15, 3-6. (Russian)

* The more recent entries in this bibliography were added by the translator.

18. ———, *Irreducible nilpotent matrix groups of prime degree,* Mat. Sb. (N.S.) **31(73)** (1952), 353-358. (Russian)

19. ———, *On nilpotent transitive subgroups of the symmetric group,* Dokl. Akad. Nauk SSSR **99**(1954), 23-25. (Russian)

20. ———, *On irreducible matrix groups,* Mat. Sb. (N.S.) **35(77)** (1954), 501-512. (Russian)

21. ———, *Locally nilpotent irreducible subgroups of the full linear group,* Dokl. Akad. Nauk SSSR **102**(1955), 41-44. (Russian)

22. ———, *On a property of nilpotent matrix groups,* Izv. Akad. Nauk SSSR Ser. Mat. **19**(1955), 273-274. (Russian)

23. ———, *On linear solvable groups,* Mat. Sb. (N.S.) **41(83)** (1957), 317-322. (Russian)

24. ———, *Two theorems on reducible nilpotent linear groups,* Trudy inst. Fiz. i Mat. Akad. Nauk BSSR **1957**, no. 2, 255-259. (Russian)

25. D. Suprunenko and R. Tyškevič, *Reducible nilpotent and locally nilpotent linear groups,* Trudy Inst. Fiz. i Mat. Akad. Nauk BSSR **1959**, no. 3, 221-223. (Russian)

26. R. Tyškevič, *Linear nilpotent group with abelian derived group,* Učen. Zap. Belorussk. Gos. Univ. **1959**, no. 3(59), 79-90. (Russian)

27. ———, *On linear nilpotent groups,* Mat. Sb. (N.S.) **42(84)** (1957), 441-444. (Russian)

28. H. Zassenhaus, *Beweis eines Satzes über diskrete Gruppen,* Abh. Math. Sem. Hansische Univ. **12**(1938), 289-312.

29. S. N. Černikov, *Über unendliche lokal auflösbare Gruppen,* Mat. Sb. (N.S.) **7(49)** (1940), 35-64. (Russian. German summary)

30. ———, *Nilpotent groups,* Proc. 3rd all-Union Math. Conf. (Moscow, 1956), Vol. I, pp. 37-40, Izdat. Akad. Nauk SSSR, Moscow, 1956. (Russian)

31. O. Ju. Šmidt, *On equations soluble by radicals whose degree is a power of a prime number,* Kiev, 1913. (Russian)

32. ———, *Infinite soluble groups,* Mat. Sb. (N.S.) **17(59)** (1945), 145-162. (Russian. English summary)

33. G. Bucht, *Die umfassendsten primitiven metazyklischen Kongruenzgruppen mit drei oder vier Variablen,* Ark. Mat. **11**(1916), 1-96.

34. S. Barskaja, *On the construction of primitive solvable groups,* Ukrain. Mat. Z. **3**(1951), 61-84. (Russian)

35. L. Kaloujnine, *La structure des p-groupes de Sylow des groupes symétriques finis,* Ann. Sci. École Norm. Sup. (3) **65**(1948), 239-276.

36. D. A. Suprunenko, *On nilpotent linear groups over a finite field,* Trudy Inst. Fiz. i Mat. Akad. Nauk BSSR **1959**, no. 3, 213-220. (Russian)

37. ———, *Linear p-groups,* Dokl. Akad. Nauk BSSR **4**(1960), 233-235. (Russian)

38. ———, *Real linear locally nilpotent groups,* Mat. Sb. (N.S.) **50(92)** (1960), 59-66. (Russian)

39. M. S. Garaščuk and D. A. Suprunenko, *Linear nilgroups,* Dokl. Akad. Nauk BSSR **4**(1960), 407-408. (Russian)

40. M. S. Garaščuk, *On the theory of generalized nilpotent linear groups,* Dokl. Akad. Nauk BSSR **4**(1960), 276-277. (Russian)

41. ———, *Sylow p-subgroups of periodic linear groups,* Dokl. Akad. Nauk BSSR **5**(1961), 95. (Russian)

42. B. Huppert, *Lineare auflösbare Gruppen,* Math. Z. **67**(1957), 479-518.